CONSIDERING GOD'S CREATION

TEACHER'S MANUAL

A creative biblical approach to natural science

Sixth Edition

by Susan Mortimer
and
Betty Smith

Soaring into higher learning . . .

Eagle's Wings

Educational Materials

P.O. Box 502
Duncan, OK 73534
www.EaglesWingsEd.com

First and foremost:

"Praise God from whom all blessings flow, Praise Him all creatures here below."
—the Doxology

Then, a special "thank you" to our mother, Faith Blight, to Edie Bakker, to Linda Hubel, and to Robbo Holleran for their help with editing. (Edie also contributed the ideas for *My Zoo Adventure*, and Linda caught the "enthusiasm bug" as she edited, and came up with ideas for lessons and the *Cloud Detective* page on her own. We hope this book will inspire your creativity too!) Thanks is due to our brother, Tom, for his computer expertise and the use of his laser printer!

And we want to extend loving appreciation to our husbands (Greg and Ron), and children (Sheri, Wendy, and Christopher; Adam, Andrew, Abigail, and Amos), without whom we would not have had the motivation or support to attempt this project.

Revised 1996, 1998, 1999, 2001, 2002, 2004, 2006

ISBN: 1-931292-17-5 (Teacher's Manual)
ISBN: 1-931292-18-3 (2 Volume Set)

Please visit our website for other product information: **www.EaglesWingsEd.com**

ABOUT THE AUTHORS

Sue Mortimer and Betty Smith are first and foremost Christians, wives and mothers. They have written another series together, *Alphabet Island Phonics* and *Eagle's Wings Comprehensive Handbook of Phonics*. Even knowing the work involved in such a big project, they still felt compelled to do this science program. *Considering God's Creation* has been well received and is meeting a real need in the homeschool community. Sue finished the first of her Create-a-Notebook series, *Remembering God's Awesome Acts,* in 1997, and the second, *Remembering God's Chosen Children,* in 2002. These books integrate Bible, history, creative writing and art. She is currently working on the third book, *Remembering God's Divided Kingdom*, and has lots of ideas for American History.

Sue Mortimer and her husband, Greg, were with Wycliffe Bible Translators in Dallas, Texas, and the Philippines for more than seventeen years. Sue has a B.S. degree in elementary education. She homeschooled her own three children. In addition, over the years she taught a total of twenty-eight missionary children while their parents were attending classes at the Wycliffe Center.

Betty Smith, her sister, is a registered nurse. She and her husband, Ron, have four children. They built their own home (paying for each phase as finances allowed) in rural Oklahoma and arranged their lives to be able to come to Dallas to work on writing projects with Sue for months at a time. The Smiths spent several months in the Ukraine in 1993 as lay missionaries and have continued to maintain contact with their friends there.

Sue and Betty are "missionary kids" from Mexico. They were "homeschooled" and "cottage-schooled" long before these terms became popular. If talents were a deck of cards, they feel that, even though they are sisters, each was dealt a completely different hand. Together, Sue and Betty make a great team. Betty writes music, does all the computer work to get the materials camera ready, and has good writing skills. She can also interpret Sue's scribbles. Sue has a creative mind for making worksheets that will do what they need to do for teaching a concept. She is always trying to put twice as much information on a page as will fit. Sue also does the beautiful artwork.

The authors created this program for their own children, for whom their greatest desire is that they grow up to be men and women of God. They hope that this program will be a blessing to you and your children as well. ❧

MULTI-LEVEL TEACHING
by Betty Smith

For those of you who have been blessed with a large family and/or are teaching several age groups together, this program is just what you need! Although this program is primarily directed to the elementary grade levels, there is great flexibility on either end. Begin by identifying the abilities and age characteristics of each child. And always keep this important concept in mind: When the foundation of our lives is based on the word of God, it is our privilege and responsibility to integrate that into every subject we teach our children. When we teach language, for example, we emphasize the order and systematic design of each language, and we explain that the "Word" (Jesus) became flesh to communicate God's love to us. When we teach science, the focus should be to introduce our children to the Creator through His creation.

From the very first, teach your **toddlers** to associate God with His creation. "God made the tree (the rock, the kitten)." With young children, it is critical to present unadulterated truth. When you sit your children down in front of an educational science program, be very sure that it will not be presenting a mixed message to them (such as evolutionary ideas or fantasy—perhaps one and the same). For instance, when my five-year old was watching a Moody Science video, he said to me, "Mommy, this is all true, isn't it?" I realized that he had been struggling with trying to discern what was true and what was not true in some of the science programs he had seen.

For **children under 8 or 9 years old**, the focus of science is discovery—touching, seeing, hearing and doing. They need to plant a garden and watch it grow. They need to have a pet and care for it. They need to walk through a forest and on a beach. They need to stay up late and see the moon come up. And even though their reading abilities are not fully developed, you can talk and walk them through many complicated concepts. For example, consider this simple explanation of molecules from *Considering God's Creation.*

"Everything around us is made up of small parts that we can't see without a powerful microscope. These small parts are called **molecules**. Let's pretend we are cold air molecules. When air molecules are cold, they get very close together and move very slowly. Let's put our hands down by our sides, get as close together as we can without touching one another, and move slowly around within a small area. Do you see how much space we take up? Not very much, do we? And how much do we weigh? It would be the sum of all our weights added together. Now let's pretend that the sun is warming us up and we will move a little further apart and move a little faster. We are warmer air now and take up more space, but we still weigh the same as we did when we were cold air. Now it is getting hotter and hotter, and we will move a little more quickly and a little further apart. We take up a lot more space now but we still weigh the same as we did when we were in a tiny area. For the space that it takes up, cold air weighs more than warm air because the molecules are so close together. When the molecules warm up and start moving faster, they get further apart, so the same size space becomes lighter. This process of heating and cooling of the air is what affects the direction and speed of the wind. As air cools, what happens to the air molecules? (the molecules get closer together so the air is heavier and sinks down) On the other hand, as air warms up, what happens to the air molecules? (the molecules get further apart and the air is lighter and rises) How does this cause wind? (The cold air rushes in to fill the vacuum left by the rising hot air. This movement is what causes wind.)"

By **second to sixth grade**, children usually have enough life experience to begin a more systematic approach to science. (*Considering God's Creation* was designed to accomplish this.) During the elementary school years, the goal is to develop a framework or filing system in your children's minds that will allow them to organize and process future learning. This overview of different scientific disciplines is most effectively taught through activities, songs, and hands-on review pages. Again, don't forget to emphasize spiritual applications from nature and talk about what God is teaching them about Himself through His creation. (Books by Dr. Paul Brand are especially enlightening in this regard.) Teach your children to question and test everything they read or hear and not to blindly accept it all as truth. Studying biographies will help your children learn to discern the worldview of scientists and to compare it to their own biblical standards. Prepare your children to approach science as detectives—to learn to observe, to ask questions and to draw conclusions. And remind them that there is still a universe of wonders waiting to be discovered.

Junior and senior high school students are ready to start adding much more information to their basic understanding of science. They are learning inductive as well as deductive thinking skills. If they already have a good basic understanding of science, they can begin to study these concepts in greater detail. Then, by college level, these students will be ready to spend a whole year on just microorganisms and biology at the cellular level.

This program can be applied in several distinctive ways for the older student. If the older child has not had a good background in science, this program can be used to do a thorough review of earth and life sciences and to prepare him to go on to more advanced concepts.

If the student is already well grounded in the basics, have the older student teach the class to the younger students. The scripted lessons make this easy and achievable. Besides taking some of the teaching load off your shoulders, your child will be learning valuable teaching skills. His younger siblings will also learn to look to him for leadership and direction. In addition, your child will get a good review of the information and be encouraged to do additional research as he prepares to teach the lesson.

Finally, the program can be used by an older student as a supplement for more advanced course work. For example, when my ninth grader was studying biology, and was scheduled to do a dissection of a frog, the pages from *Considering God's Creation* about amphibians were a handy review and gave him a desire to learn more.

So use this program with all your children at the same time. And when you've gone through it once, go through it again with the younger ones a couple of years later, using the DIGGING DEEPER ideas to expand the lessons. Enjoy *Considering God's Creation* with your children, and make this curriculum your servant, not your master. May your efforts and ours bring glory to God the Creator, King of the Universe and Blessed Controller of all things. &

QUESTIONS and ANSWERS

Tell me about **Considering God's Creation?** ***Considering God's Creation*** is a unique approach to natural science. We have tried to keep the activities simple so that you will not need a lot of materials or equipment. Most of the work is done for you! We have done the research (reviewing hundreds of books), and have created **effective games, experiments, poems, songs, arts and crafts projects, and notebook pages**. The notebook pages are designed to **help your students become true scientists, carefully observing and investigating God's creation**. In addition, we have placed a **strong emphasis on integrating science with the Bible**.

May I photocopy the notebook pages? This is a family business with limited resources. If you appreciate our efforts and would like us to continue to create new products, please limit photocopying to your immediate family or class. Thank you! We do have reasonably priced student notebooks available. You might consider purchasing a book for each student as there are over a hundred and ninety pages that need to be copied and three-hole punched. Several pages are identical because they will be used more than one time. The pages to cut out and glue are blank on the back, except for a page number.

What other supplies will I need besides this book? Additional items that each student will need include: a three-ring binder (if you are photocopying the pages), scissors, glue, crayons, pencils, and pen. A few other items will be used, such as eggs, pans, ice, flour, a good flashlight and so forth. These will be listed as needed under the PREPARATION headings.

You might consider purchasing a field guide for flowers, trees, and rocks. The "Golden" pocket field guides are inexpensive and work well. Encyclopedias or library books may be used if preferred. We have also included a list of optional resources in the DIGGING DEEPER sections of each lesson as well as in the ADDITIONAL RESOURCE SUGGESTIONS at the back of this book. Or you may use whatever materials and textbooks you have on hand. **This program, however, may be used without additional resources.**

How do I go about teaching a lesson? There are enough lessons included to allow for one lesson a week for an entire school year. (However, many of the lessons have several parts and it would be beneficial, especially with younger children, to spend two to three years covering the material.) The lesson may be done in one long class period, and then reviewed at intervals during the week, or it may be divided into smaller portions. A general lesson plan is included on page 10, entitled BASIC TEACHING PROCEDURE. Most of the text in the teacher's manual is written for you to read aloud. Teacher's instructions are italicized. Answers to questions are generally enclosed in brackets.

I already have a science curriculum. Can I use this program with it? Certainly! Locate the sections that correspond to the material you are covering, and use what fits.

How can I adapt the program for younger and older students? Although this science program is geared primarily for second grade to seventh grade, it can be adapted to the child. If you are teaching young children, you may need to help them with the notebook pages and paraphrase the information for their level. For older children, use the DIGGING DEEPER for ideas to keep them challenged. Twelve CROSSWORD REVIEW pages are now included in the student notebook and may be used for review or as tests for older children.

TABLE OF CONTENTS

Bold-faced numbers indicate *Considering God's Creation* Teacher's Manual page number.
Italic numbers indicate *notebook* page number, located in the student notebook.

About the Authors i
Multi-Level Teaching ii
Questions and Answers iv
Table of Contents v
Introduction ix
Basic Teaching Procedure x

CREATION

LESSON 1: Creation 1
    Considering God's Creation Cover
    And God Was Pleased, p. 3
    Not by Chance, pp. 4-6

THE UNIVERSE: STARS, SUN and PLANETS

LESSON 2: My Place in the Universe 5
    Considering God's Universe, pp. 7, 9-10
    Star Slides, p. 11-12
    Scientist Detective, p. 8
LESSON 3: Our Solar System 7
    The Planets, pp. 13-18
LESSON 4: Getting to Know the Planets 9
    Solar System Detective, pp. 19-27

THE EARTH

LESSON 5: Our Planet Earth 15
    The Earth, pp. 28-30
Lesson 5:A Light 16
Lesson 5:B The Earth 17
Lesson 5:C The Atmosphere 18

NON-LIVING THINGS: ROCKS and MINERALS

LESSON 6: Rocks 21
Lesson 6:A Igneous Rock 21
Lesson 6:B Sedimentary and Metamorphic Rock 22
    The Rock Cycle, pp. 31, 33-34
Lesson 6:C Becoming a Rock Detective 24
    Rock Detective, pp. 32, 35-37
    Scientist Detective, p. 38

WEATHER

LESSON 7: Weather 27
Lesson 7:A Sun and Weather 27
Lesson 7:B Air and Weather 28
Lesson 7:C Water and Weather 29
Lesson 7:D Rotation and Weather 30
Lesson 7:E Land and Weather 30
  Weather Recipe, pp. 39, 41-42
LESSON 8: Clouds 32
  Cloud Cover, p. 40
  Cloud Detective, p. 43-46
  Two Week Weather Chart, p. 49
LESSON 9: The Speed of Light, Sound and Wind 34
  Scientist Detective, p. 48
  Speed Detective, p. 49

THE PLANT KINGDOM

LESSON 10: Plants 37
Lesson 10:A Photosynthetic Plants 37
Lesson 10:B Flowers 38
  Plant Parts, pp. 50-52
  Portrait of a Flower, pp. 54, 56, 58, 60, 62
  Flower Detective, pp. 55, 57, 59, 61, 63
  Scientist Detective, p. 64
Lesson 10:C Fungus Plants 42
  Mold Detective, p. 65
LESSON 11: Trees 45
  Sktech of a Tree, pp. 66,68, 70, 72, 74
  Tree Detective, pp. 67, 69, 71, 73, 75
LESSON 12: Plant Ecology—Flora and Fauna 47
  Plant Life on our Planet, p. 76

THE ANIMAL KINGDOM

LESSON 13: Insects 49
  Insect Detective, p. 77
  The Life Cycles of Insects, pp. 78-80
  Making Sense of Insects, pp. 79-81
LESSON 14: Spiders 52
  Caught in a Spider's Web, p. 82

LESSON 15: Introduction 54
  Animal Classmates Game, pp. 83-88
  Features of Creatures, pp. 89-92
  Scientist Detective, p. 93

LESSON 16: Fish **56**
    Word Search—FISH, p. 94
    Animal Detective, pp. 95-98
    The Deep Blue Sea, pp. 99, 101-102
LESSON 17: Reptiles **59**
    Word Search—REPTILES, p. 100
    Animal Detective, p. 103, 97-98
    Representing Reptiles, pp. 104-106
    Scientist Detective, p. 107
LESSON 18: Birds **61**
    Word Search—BIRDS, p. 108
    Animal Detective, p. 109, 97-98
LESSON 19: Mammals **63**
    Word Search—MAMMALS, p. 110
    Animal Detective, p. 111, 97-98
    Scientist Detective, p. 112
LESSON 20: Zoo Adventure **65**
    My Zoo Adventure, pp. 113, 115, 117, 119, 121, 123, 125, 127, 129
    Zoo Creatures, pp. 114, 116, 118, 120, 122, 124, 126, 128
LESSON 21: Amphibians **69**
    Amphibian Detective, pp. 130-132

ANIMAL ANATOMY & PHYSIOLOGY

LESSON 22: Animal Structure **71**
    Scientist Detective, p. 134
    A Pile of Bones, pp. 133, 135-136
    Horns and Antlers, pp. 135-138
    Birds in Flight, pp. 139-142
    Animal Tracks Game, pp. 143-148
    My Animal Tracks Book, pp. 149-152
    Locomotion, pp. 153-154
    Horse in Motion, pp. 155-156
LESSON 23: Animal Food Chain **75**
    Scientist Detective, p. 158
    What Percent is Water? p. 157
    Beaks and Feet Show Where Birds Live and What They Eat, pp. 159-162
    Cud Chewers and Meat Eaters, pp. 163-166
    Forest Food Chain, p. 167
    Scientist Detective, p. 168
    Prey for a Year, pp. 169-172
    Feeding the Multitudes, pp. 173-176
LESSON 24: Animal Reproduction/Genetics **78**
    Each After Its Own Kind, pp. 177-182
    Egg Factory, pp. 183-186
    The Kingdom Of Living Things, pp. 187-190

Classifying Animals, pp. 191-192
Guess Genes for Guinea Pigs, p. 193
Breeding Domestic Chickens, p. 194
LESSON 25: Animal Instinct, Vision and Brains 83
Migration, pp. 195-198
The Eyes Have It, pp. 199-202
Brains, p. 203
LESSON 26: Animal Ecology 85
Lesson 26 A: Extinction 85
Extinct is Forever, pp. 204-206
Lesson 26 B: Whales 87
A Whale of Information, p. 207

MAN: MADE IN GOD'S IMAGE

LESSON 27: Man—Reproductive System 91
Wonderfully Made, pp. 208-210
LESSON 28: The Cell 94
Cell City, pp. 211-216
LESSON 29: Man—Skeletal System 96
God Made Me, p. 217-226
LESSON 30: Man—Digestive System 98
God Made Me, pp. 227-230
The Digestive System, pp. 231, 233-234
LESSON 31: Man—Circulatory System 101
God Made Me, pp. 229-230
LESSON 32: Man—Respiratory System 104
God Made Me, pp. 229-230
LESSON 33: Man—Nervous System 106
The Human Brain, pp. 232-234
Automatic Pilot, p. 235
LESSON 34: Man—Integumentary System 108
Scientist Detective, p. 238
Skin Deep, pp. 237, 239-240
Fingerprint Detective Game, pp. 237, 239-240
LESSON 35: Man—Endocrine System and Excretory System 111
God Made Me, pp. 229-230
LESSON 36: Man—Muscular System 113
Scientist Detective, p. 242
The Inside Story, pp. 241, 243-244

MISCELLANEOUS

SCIENTISTS: *Scientist Detective, pp. 8, 38, 48, 53, 64, 93, 107, 112, 134, 158, 168, 238, 242*
REVIEWS: *Crossword Reviews, pp. 245-256*
ADDITIONAL RESOURCE SUGGESTIONS 116
SELECTED BIBLIOGRAPHY 119
ANSWERS TO WORD SEARCHES 122
ANSWERS TO CROSSWORD REVIEWS 123

INTRODUCTION

The purpose of this book is to provide an introduction to the Creator through His creation. This is an extremely flexible program. It may be used alone as a complete one to three-year study. It may also be used with any other science program by selecting the areas that apply to what is being studied. This program is not set up by grade level, so it can be easily adapted to multiple levels of students. A relatively small amount of reading is required to help keep complicated concepts at an introductory level while still pursuing scientific observation and analysis. Consequently it can be used in a single grade classroom or a multi-level classroom. It can also be an excellent family project. This book is designed to provide you with a low cost, high quality product that will bring your students pride and pleasure. Our sincere desire is that this program will captivate children with God's amazing creation and open windows of knowledge for them so that they will hunger to learn more.

We have kept the activities simple so that you will not need a lot of materials or equipment. Most of the work is done for you! We have done the research (reviewing hundreds of books), and have created effective games, experiments, poems, songs, arts and crafts projects, and notebook pages. The notebook pages are designed to **help your students become true scientists, carefully observing and investigating God's creation**. In addition, we have placed a strong emphasis on relating science to the Bible. You, the teacher, have control over the information being taught since you will be reading most of it aloud. You have the opportunity to "edit" or add to the text to make it appropriate for your particular student. You also have the option to introduce the material in a different order or to delete a page if you wish. Although this book can stand alone, you may use any additional resources you have available or the ones suggested in the DIGGING DEEPER sections. For planning purposes, we have compiled these suggestions in the ADDITIONAL RESOURCE SUGGESTIONS in the back of this manual.

Considering God's Creation is a unique approach to teaching science. Traditional science programs are often limited to reading assignments that focus primarily on comprehension and vocabulary. *Considering God's Creation* can breathe new life into such programs, providing creative ways to interact with the information in their texts. The non-traditional "hands-on" science programs provide many creative ideas but often call for materials that are difficult to obtain and require a tremendous amount of work on the part of the instructor. Afterwards, the finished science projects are hard to store. *Considering God's Creation* has solved these problems for you, since even the best instructors are short on time, energy and money. *Considering God's Creation* invites creativity but keeps clutter to a minimum. Each student creates a notebook that is simple to store and impressive to show to family and friends.

Although this program provides a good foundation for natural science, **remind your students that this just the beginning**. Research papers, vocabulary tests, and book reports can be added to the notebook. We want to emphasize an open-ended approach and to inspire each student to continue learning on his own.

As scientists discover more about the universe, they find new information that changes their previous assumptions. Your students will find many contradictions in the different books as they study, so it is important to teach them to question and test the materials and not to blindly believe everything they read or hear as truth. So many "educational" books and documentaries portray a world that happened "by chance", where man is merely an animal and evolution and chaos are the universal driving forces. This program teaches them how to watch out for the promotion of ungodly ideas. All the answers are not in yet, nor will they be until we see God face to face. Until then it is time to claim back territory that has been taken by the enemy of God!

BASIC TEACHING PROCEDURE

Below are some general guidelines to follow for each lesson. The primary teaching tool is the **NOTEBOOK**, which enables the students to interact with science in a way that promotes deep understanding. Students will discover information automatically as they do the activities, using the lesson text as a resource. **The lesson in the Teacher's Manual may be read aloud, discussed, or used merely to suggest further activities.** Directions to the teacher are generally in italics and are not to be read aloud. Answers are included in brackets following the questions.

Procedure for Teacher	Check List for Student
PREPARATION: Review lesson and collect any needed materials for the activities and notebooks. Obtain the appropriate notebook pages for each student. Also, select assignments from the **Digging Deeper** section before class for older students.	☑ I have my pencil, crayons, glue, notebook and scissors.
VOCABULARY: Use flash cards or write the vocabulary words on the board. Discuss the meanings and practice using them in sentences. Have older children use the words for spelling. (Key: Ger./German, Gk./Greek, L./Latin, O.E./Old English, Russ./Russian)	☑ I can define, spell and use new words.
INTRODUCTION: This section will give an overview of the lesson and materials to be covered. It may be read aloud for older children or paraphrased for younger students.	☑ I can tell about the subject.
SONG/POEM: An original song or poem which illustrates new concepts from the lesson. (An audio CD with the songs is included with the Teacher's Manual.)	☑ I can say or sing the poem.
ACTIVITY: These activities help the student to further understand the concepts. Other experiments or activities may be added as desired.	☑ I can explain the new concept.
BIBLE READING: Have the student locate the Scriptures prior to reading through this section. Occasionally do "Sword Drills" (i.e., see which student can find the verse first). Then read and discuss the verses, focusing on seeing God as the Creator in nature. A concordance may be helpful for further study.	☑ I can tell how God views and relates to His creation and am learning more about His character through creation.
NOTEBOOK: The notebook is a concise summary of the materials presented in a creative way so that the student can interact with the information and gain a deeper understanding of it. Many pages are designed to allow the student to discover the information as he does it and follow up with a discussion about the completed page. Give as little information as possible before doing the notebook page, then give additional information in the discussion time.	☑ I have completed and understand my notebook page.
EVOLUTION STUMPERS: These are scientific facts that support creation and question evolution in a positive way. *Unlocking the Mysteries of Creation*, by Dennis R. Petersen, was a great resource.	☑ I can support my stand on creation.
REVIEW: This portion of the lesson continues and reinforces learning. A list of questions is included for discussion. The student is also encouraged to explain his notebook page to someone. Twelve **Crossword Reviews** are included in the student notebook to be used as directed for testing or review with older students.	☑ I have explained my notebook page to a friend or relative.
DIGGING DEEPER: These are ideas for further study, research and discovery. They often require outside resources and books. The **Scientist Detective** pages are designed to reveal the foundation from which a scientist based his investigations. *For Those Who Dare, 101 Great Christians And How They Changed The World* by John Hudson Tiner, and other books by the same author are excellent resources.	☑ I am learning more on my own.

CREATION

LESSON 1: Creation

PREPARATION: *Each student will need an individual notebook OR a **copy of notebook pp. 3-6**, and a three-ring binder. In addition, he will need a pencil, crayons, glue, and scissors. Vocabulary words may be written on flash cards.*

VOCABULARY:
> **consider**: To ponder, contemplate with awe, think about deeply
> [L. *considerare*, observe]
> **creation**: All that which is created [L. *craere*, to make out of nothing]

INTRODUCTION: Creation is one of the basic foundations of our Christian faith. Without a clear understanding of God as the Creator, we have no clear basis for a need for God. If there is no Creator, there is no ultimate authority and no absolute regarding good and evil. Consequently, according to this line of thinking, there is no sin and no need for a savior. But, praise God, He is the Creator, the Authority and He has provided the Savior.

Over the next few weeks, we will consider the totally awesome things that God has created. As we study creation, we will learn about God, who created it all. When we see the exact order in which He made things, we will find that nothing happened by accident or chance. We will learn to look carefully at the world around us and to see the things that are similar and the things that are different. We won't be able to learn about everything at one time. The truth is that no person knows everything about anything and never will. But as we study, God will open our eyes and help us to see more and more about our world and about Himself. You may even discover things that no person has ever noticed before. Some authors of science and nature books sound as though they have all the answers, and many have tried to disprove the Bible. However, through the years, new bits of information keep being discovered, proving that what such "experts" once said were "facts" were actually wrong, and what the Bible said was really true all along. So as we go on this adventure together, let's keep our eyes open and our minds alert to be ready to see what we can discover.

SONG/POEM: *(Open to the notebook pages* Considering God's Creation Cover *and* And God Was Pleased, *p. 3. Read the poem together, then listen and sing along with the CD. Then have the student draw and color pictures in the circles representing each day of creation.)*

> **And God Was Pleased!**
> On the first day of creation,
> God made the dark and light,
> And He called it day and night.
> And God was pleased.
>
> On the second day of creation,
> God made the water and the air,

And this was the atmosphere.
And God was pleased.

On the third day of creation,
God made the land and sea,
And every plant, flower, grass, and tree.
And God was pleased.

On the fourth day of creation,
God made the stars, the moon, the sun,
Thus the seasons were begun.
And God was pleased.

On the fifth day of creation,
God made the birds and fish,
And any sea creature you could wish.
And God was pleased.

On the sixth day of creation,
God made animals fill the land,
Then He formed man with His hand.
And God was pleased.

On the seventh day of creation,
God looked at what He'd done,
And rested to enjoy each one.
And God was pleased.

BIBLE READING: *(Have student look up Scriptures.)* The Bible is full of references to God as the Creator of all things. Chapter 1 of Genesis gives us a detailed account of the order of creation and Chapter 2 focuses on the creation of man in the image of God. All things were created by and for Him (Hebrews 11:3; John 1:1–4). Romans 1:18–32 shows us the natural consequences of unbelief in God as the Creator. Many people throughout history and even today have been in such awe of God's creation that they have worshipped it instead of God. God does not want us to worship His creation but Himself (Romans 1:21–25). In fact, as scientists discover more and more things about the world around us, the facts only show us more about the incredible power and wisdom of God. People might be able to observe and define what they see, but were they there when it was created? Have they ever caused the sun to rise (Job 37:12)? Or do the eagles fly and make nests at their command (Job 39:27)? God not only created this world, but He is the One who keeps it running. It is God's intent to show Himself to us through His creation and to display His very nature to us (Romans 1:20). So, whenever you are studying God's creation, you are learning something new about what God is like.

NOTEBOOK: You will make some special projects over the next year. These projects will all go into your own notebook that you can use to teach your family and friends the things you are learning. I want you to do your best work on these pages so that you can be proud of them. Some of the pages will be pop-up pages or have little booklets to look through. Other pages are called "Detective" pages. These pages will help you learn to be a true scientist, carefully looking at and investigating God's creation.

Do you know that some people think that the universe and the Earth happened just by chance? But the Bible tells us clearly that God made it all—and just by the work of His fingers (Psalm 8: 3). Even the order in which He created things shows us a specific plan. Open your Bible to the first chapter of Genesis and let's read the record of creation together again. *(Read Genesis 1.)*

(The following questions are to help give direction for a discussion with your student. Possible answers are included in brackets, but these may vary.) Let's talk about creation together and ask some questions about what could have happened at each point in creation if things had been different. Creation had to have a beginning. What if there was no God? [*There would be no creation. He created the entire universe from nothing.*] What if there was no light? [*There would be no light, heat, or energy for plants to grow.*] What if there was no water or atmosphere? [*The earth would be as barren and dead as the moon.*] What if there was no land? [*No land animals or plants could exist.*] What if there were no plants? [*There would be no food or oxygen for animals because only plants make their own food and oxygen.*] What if there were no sun, moon or stars? [*There would be no energy to run the world, no seasons, and none of the cycles that life depends on.*]

Although the Genesis account of creation was written about 4,000 years ago, even scientists who don't believe in the Bible agree that the general order of creation told to us in the Bible is an accurate description of how things could have happened. Not only were things created in this order, but it was God who told mankind how He did it. Other religions (including the religion of "evolution") have "fables" that people have made up to try to explain how the universe came to be. These are in no way supported by scientific facts. If the author of Genesis had wildly guessed about how God created the universe, the chance of his guessing this particular order is only one in about three and one half million (or the odds of randomly drawing ten numbers in correct numerical sequence; 1:3,628,000).

Not by Chance, pp. 4-6. Let's try those chances ourselves with our notebook page, *Not by Chance.* On *Not by Chance (page 2)* are all the different aspects we have discussed about creation. They are numbered from one to ten. Color the pictures, then cut them out along the dotted lines. Now turn the cards upside down and mix them up. Close your eyes and choose one at a time, writing down the order that you come up with on the *Not by Chance* page. Then we will discuss whether creation could have happened in that order. Do the same thing three times. Without looking, it is impossible to get them in just the right order. Next, glue the pictures in the correct order on the page. Remember! Creation didn't happen just by chance or accident, but God created all things in an orderly manner.

EVOLUTION STUMPERS: For something like our universe to exist today, what had to be there before it began? Nothing can begin from nothing. There had to be something to start the universe with all its stars and planets. What was that something that began the universe? Was it "matter" or was it God? Either position takes faith to believe in it. And both are religious statements. One religion states, "In the beginning, God created the heavens and the earth." Genesis 1:1. The other religion states, "Once upon a time there was the 'Big Bang.'"

REVIEW: 1. What did God create on each day of creation? [*first day—dark and light; second day—water and air; third day—land and sea, plants, flowers, grass, and trees; fourth day—stars, moon, sun; fifth day—birds and fish, sea creatures; sixth day—land animals and man; seventh day—God rested*]
2. What did God create to mark the seasons? [*Gen. 1:14, the stars, the moon, and the sun were created to designate the seasons*]
3. What did God create in His own image? [*man—mankind, i.e., Adam and Eve*]
4. What did God use to make man? [*the dust of the ground*]

Have the student explain his notebook page to a friend or relative and tell what he learned from that lesson. Also, review the songs/poems and activities.

DIGGING DEEPER: 1. Write a "newspaper article" to show evidence for creation. 2. Do a book report on a book about creation such as *Science and the Bible*, by Henry M. Morris, *Unlocking the Mysteries of Creation*, by Dennis R. Petersen, Creation Resource Foundation, Box 570, El Dorado, CA, 95623, or *In The Beginning: Compelling Evidence for Creation and the Flood*, by Walt Brown, Center for Scientific Creation, 5612 N. 20th Place, Phoenix, AZ, 85016, 1995. 3. Visit the Creation Evidence Museum, P.O. Box 309, Glen Rose, Texas 76043-0309. 4. Make a list of the things that God says about Himself as the Creator in Job 37–39. 5. For more information about creation and science write to the Answers in Genesis Ministries, Ken Ham, PO Box 6330, Florence, KY 41022-6330. (www.answersingenesis.org) 6. Listen to a seminar by Catie Frates, *Revealing Evidences for Creation* from Censored Science, 803 Coleman Dr., Plant City, FL, 33567. 7. Watch a video, such as *The Young Age of the Earth*, AlphaProductions, 1994, (available from Earth Science Associates, P.O.Box 12067, Knoxville, TN, 37912-0067), or *Evolution, Fact or Fiction,* Roger Oakland, Oakland Communications, Inc., 1992.

THE UNIVERSE: STARS, SUN and PLANETS

LESSON 2: My Place in the Universe

PREPARATION: *Student will need* **notebook pp. 7-12 (p. 8 will not be needed until Lesson 3)**, *scissors, scotch tape, crayons, an empty oatmeal, cereal or shoe box, and a flashlight. Vocabulary words may be written on flash cards.*

VOCABULARY:

>**constellation:** a fixed group of stars [L. *cum*, together + *stella*, a star]
>
>**continent**: large mass of land [L. *cum*, together + *tenere*, to hold]
>
>**galaxy**: a group or system of stars and other heavenly bodies
>>[Gk. *galac*, milk; galaxy = milky circle, hence, Milky Way Galaxy]
>
>**planet**: a heavenly body that revolves around the sun [Gk. *plane*, to wander;
>>planet = to wander in the sky]
>
>**solar system**: the group of planets, their satellites (moons), comets, meteors,
>>asteroids, and so forth, that revolves around the sun [L. *sol*, sun]
>
>**star**: any celestial body that gives off light [L. *stella*, a star]
>
>**universe**: all created things [L. *unus*, one + *versum,* to turn]

INTRODUCTION: Have you ever been outside on a very dark night and looked up at the stars? What do they look like? [*They look like tiny pinpoints of light.*] A **star** appears to us to be a fixed point of light in the sky. Stars seem to be very small because they are so far away.   Have you tried to count them? [*It is impossible to count them all.*] Even if you had a special telescope with cameras and computers to help you, you would find that each time you looked closer, you would discover more and more objects in the heavens. Many of those sparkling lights in the sky are not a just single star but billions of them—so far away that they look like a single dim point of light. If you could be on one of those stars, our sun and earth would look like a single dot too. Throughout the ages, men have tried to count the stars. An ancient Greek, Ptolemy, counted 1,056. In the 1600's, Johannes Kepler, came up with 1,005. If we counted all the stars visible from everywhere on the Earth, we might reach a total of 6,000 stars if we had endless patience and very good eyesight. But with the telescopes that are now available, astronomers estimate that there are at least a hundred-million-billion-billion (10^{26}) stars. We could never count them all! Did you know that the sun is a star? Many stars are much larger than our sun.

SONG/POEM:

>**Day and Night**
>God made the sun to rule the day,
>God made the moon to rule the night,
>And when we go to Heaven one day,
>Jesus alone will be our Light.

ACTIVITY: In early times, people looked at the stars and, like a dot-to-dot picture, they imagined different shapes and pictures that they could see in groups of stars. In one group of stars they thought they could see a bear, in another a hunter, and in still another, a fish. The people made up stories about these stars to explain how the world was created and controlled. Many of them believed the stars affected what happened in their lives. They could also tell directions by where the stars were in the sky.

Constellations are groups of stars that have names corresponding to the shapes that people saw in the sky. We are going to look at some "slides" of constellations today. Cut out the squares of constellations from the *Star Slides, pp. 11-12.* Carefully poke holes in each star with a pencil or nail. To make a "slide projector", cut out a square hole slightly smaller than the star "slides" on one end of the cardboard box. Directly across from the hole and about two inches lower, cut a circle for the flashlight to fit through. Put the flashlight in the hole. Attach one "slide" at a time over the square hole on the outside of the box with a small piece of tape. Darken the room and turn on the flashlight. Direct the angle of the flashlight so that the light reflects off the inside of the box and does not shine directly at the "slide." What do you think they look like? What would you name them? What is the name that has been given to them? Repeat this with the rest of the star "slides."

NOTEBOOK: *Considering God's Universe, pp. 7, 9-10. (Younger children may need help.)* Color the pictures, then cut and carefully glue or tape the pages from *Considering God's Universe (page 2)* onto the *Considering God's Universe* page. *(A cotton-tipped swab works well for putting on the exact amount of glue where it is needed.)* Glue on the booklet pages starting with the smallest page first (10, 9, 8 and so forth). Make sure each page can open freely. Then fill in the blanks to the story, using the words from the corresponding page number. When you finish, let's read the story out loud together and discuss it. *[Answers: 1. Milky Way Galaxy. 2. Solar System. 3. Earth. 4. North America. 5. United States. 6. Colorado. 7. Rocky Mountains. 8. Pike's Peak. 9. forest. 10. tree. 11. me.] (Read the following along with your students and have them fill in the underlined answers in unison.)* In God's immense Universe, among the innumerable galaxies, is our galaxy, the Milky Way Galaxy. In the Milky Way Galaxy, with all its billions of stars, is our star and its planets called the Solar System. Out of the nine planets in our Solar System, only one, the Earth, can support life. On Earth, with all its oceans and lands, is a continent called North America. There in North America is a country called the United States. In the United States, one of fifty states is Colorado. Through Colorado is a ridge of tall, rugged mountains known as the Rocky Mountains. In the Rocky Mountains is a tall mountain called Pike's Peak. On Pike's Peak is a forest with lots of trees. In that forest is a particular pine tree. Sitting under the shade of that tree is me. And I am considering, pondering and contemplating God's immense Universe.

BIBLE READING: *(Have student look up Scriptures.)* The word "consider" means to carefully think about something. When we go outside at night and look at all the stars above us, it is breathtaking to consider the fact that the Creator of all the universe cares about us. David, the king, was awestruck when he thought about the moon and the stars. He could hardly believe that God even thinks about man (Psalm 8:3). All of creation shows us the glory of God (Psalm 19:1; Romans 1:20). Think of trying to count every grain of sand in the world! It would be something like trying to count the stars (Jeremiah 33:22). And just imagine! God knows each of them by name (Isaiah 40:26; Psalm 147:4)! He created each one to be unique (1 Corinthians 15:41). The stars were created to praise God (Psalm 148:1–6), to sing together (Job 38:7), and they even foretold Jesus' birth (Matthew 2:2,9,10). And the God who created all of this cares about us. His thoughts toward us outnumber the sand (Psalm 139:17–18). He loves us so much that He gave His Son, Jesus Christ to be our Savior (John 3:16).

EVOLUTION STUMPERS: If you blew up a stack of lumber, would it result in a five-story mansion? To have a universe that is precisely designed, could something have just exploded? And what would that something have been? How did it come into existence if there was no Creator?

REVIEW: 1. What is the universe? [*all created things*]
2. How many stars are there? [*we don't know, but more than we can even count*]
3. What is a galaxy? [*a group of stars and other heavenly bodies*]
4. What is the solar system? [*the group of planets and other heavenly bodies that revolve around the sun*]
5. How many planets are there in our solar system? [*nine*]
6. What is a continent? [*a large mass of land*]
Have the student explain his notebook page to a friend or relative and tell what he learned from the lesson. Also, review the songs.

DIGGING DEEPER: 1. Learn to identify at least three constellations. (A good way to get started is with a book called *Your Guide to the Sky,* by Rick Shaffer, Lowell House, Los Angeles, CA, 1994.)   2. Go outside (or camp out) on a clear, dark night and count stars. 3. Paint or glue "glow-in-the-dark" stars in the shapes of constellations on your bedroom ceiling. 4. Do a research paper on the different types of galaxies. 5. Visit a planetarium. 6. People who believe in astrology believe that they can foretell the unknown by the position of the stars. See what the Bible has to say about this and write a report about your findings (Deuteronomy 4:19, 17:2–5, 18:10–12; Isaiah 47:12–15; Jeremiah 8:1–2; Daniel 2:19–30). 7. Enjoy *Astronomy and the Bible, Questions and Answers* by Donald B. DeYoung, Baker Book House, Grand Rapids, MI, 1989. 8. Study other types of heavenly bodies, such as comets, meteors and meteorites. 9. Read Chapter 18, "The Prompter" from *In His Image,* by Dr. Paul Brand & Phillip Yancy, Zondervan Publishing House, Grand Rapids, MI, 1984, and then research navigating by the stars. 10. Check out *The Astronomy Book* by Dr. Jonathan Henry, Master Books, Green Forest, AR, 1999.

LESSON 3: Our Solar System

PREPARATION: *Student will need **notebook pp. 13-18**, scissors, thread, scotch tape, and crayons. Vocabulary words may be written on flash cards. [For older students, use* Scientist Detective, *p. 8 as directed in the* DIGGING DEEPER *section].*

VOCABULARY:
        gravity: the force that attracts one object to another [L. *gravitas,* heavy]
        orbit: the path of a heavenly body as it rotates around another body [L. *orbis,* a circle]

INTRODUCTION and ACTIVITY: The sun is at the center of our solar system and all the planets orbit around it. The sun warms us and causes plants to grow. It is the sun that dictates day and night, winter and spring. It has enough pull to hold nine planets in orbit. The sun is 740 times bigger and heavier than all the planets put together. The sun could hold 1,170,000 earths. However the sun is an ordinary star. It is not a large star nor is it an extra hot star. The sun is just a lot closer to us than any other star. It is 300,000 times closer than the next nearest star.

We are going to do a little experiment so that you will better understand what an orbit and gravity are. Hold my hand and try to run in a straight line. *(Teacher will stand in one spot and pivot in a circle, keeping hold of child's hand. The child will try to run in a straight line but will end up going in a circle around the teacher since there is a pull between them. Repeat with others in class.)* Do you see what happened? You couldn't go straight ahead because I was holding onto you. You had to go in a circle around me. The planets and the sun have an invisible hold on each other. This hold is called **gravity**. It keeps the planets going around the sun in an **orbit** or circle. Planets would move in a straight line except for the pull of the sun. The sun is so much larger than the planets that it has a strong hold. But some of the larger planets also have a pull on the sun that causes the sun to "wobble" a bit. *(This principle may have been demonstrated if a large child caused you to move and not be able to stay in one place while he was "orbiting" around you. This is what happens with the gravitational pull of the larger planets.)* The moon is pulled in an orbit around the earth. The moon's gravity has a pull on the earth. This pull causes water to get "pulled up", making the tides.

There are nine planets in our solar system. Although to us the planets look like stars in the sky, people who have watched the skies throughout history noticed that these bodies move around differently than the stars do. They called them planets, which means 'wanderers.' Each of the planets is orbiting, or going around the sun, which is actually our nearest star. The planets also have smaller bodies called "satellites" or "moons" orbiting around them. The earth has one such moon, while other planets have more and Mercury and Venus have none.

Here is a poem to help you learn the names of the planets in order from the sun. The eighth and ninth planets' orbits overlap and so they changed positions from 1989 to 1999. It will be many, many years before they reverse positions again.

SONG/POEM:

    The Planets
    The planets starting from the sun are Mercury and Venus,
    The Earth, then Mars and Jupiter, and Saturn and Uranus.
    The next in line is Neptune and Pluto after that,
    The Lord our God fixed them in space,
    And He keeps them all in place.

BIBLE READING: *(Have student look up Scriptures.)* The earth, sun, moon and stars follow the pathways that God has set for them. Johannes Kepler described this intricate mathematical pattern as the "harmony of the spheres." Today as scientists study the stars, they have found that the stars emit waves or sounds. They really do sing the praises of their Creator (Job 38:7). They seem to hang on nothing (Job 26:7). And the intricate relationship of these patterns brings us the seasons, day and night, cold and heat (Genesis 8:22; Jeremiah 5:24). As immense as the universe seems to be, God says that heaven is just His throne and that the earth is like His footstool (Isaiah 66:1). To us it seems that the universe will always be there, but God has told us that heaven and earth will pass away, but that His words will not (Mark 13:31; 2 Peter 3:7–12). God is creating a new heaven and a new earth (Isaiah 65:17; Revelation 21:1; 2 Peter 2: 14). And all creation is waiting for its completion in Jesus Christ (Romans 8:19–22) and for the time that we will be able to see Him face to face (1 Corinthians 13:12; Colossians 2:16–17). When we are with Jesus, there will no longer be a need for the sun, moon, and stars as we know them, for the Bible tells us that Jesus will be our Light (Revelation 21:23, 22:5).

NOTEBOOK: *The Planets, pp. 13-18.* Cut along the dotted line of *The Planets (page 2)* and glue it onto the top of *The Planets* page. On *The Planets (page 3),* color each of the planets according to the indicated colors. Cut them out on the dotted lines. Then tape a two to four inch piece of thread at the center top of each planet, behind the planet's name. Fold on the solid line and glue the insides of the circles together. Then tape the top of the string or thread over the correct number on *The Planets (page 2).* To look at the planets hanging in space, hold *The Planets* page vertically and lift *The Planets (page 2)* horizontally. The planets will all hang down in the correct order. If the planets hang down below the page when it is closed, shorten their strings.

EVOLUTION STUMPERS: Over the past 100 years, scientists have discovered that the sun is shrinking about 5 feet every hour. If the sun had existed 20 million years ago (the length of time evolutionists say is needed for animals to have evolved from the "primeval soup"), the sun would have had to be so large that its surface would have touched the earth. What effect would that have had on the earth? Would there be an earth at all?

DIGGING DEEPER: 1. Fill out a *Scientist Detective* page (*notebook p. 8*) for one of these scientists: Ptolemy (100's), Sir Isaac Newton (1642–1727) or Edwin Hubble (1889–1953). 2. Read and think about some of the ideas in the book, *The Gospel in the Stars*, by Joseph A. Seiss, Kregel Publications, Grand Rapids, MI, 49501, 1972. 3. Watch the videos, *Journeys to the Edge of Creation: I. Our Solar System; II. The Milky Way & Beyond,* by Moody Institute of Science, 820 N. LaSalle Blvd, Chicago, IL, 60610. 4. Check the Internet for listings under "Solar System" and "Planets." 5. Study *Creation Astronomy: A Study Guide to the Constellations!* by F. Gerwitz & J. Whitlock, Media Angels, 15720 S. Pebble Lane, Fort Myers, FL, 33912-2341.

LESSON 4: Getting to Know the Planets

PREPARATION: *Student will need **notebook pp. 19-27**, pencils and crayons. You will need a spinning top **or** a **hard boiled** egg. Vocabulary words may be written on flash cards.*

VOCABULARY:
    AU (astronomical unit): the distance from the sun to Earth (about 93,000,000 miles)
    axis: an imaginary line passing through the center of the earth from the North pole to the South pole [L. *axis*, an axle]
    day: the length of time it takes a planet to rotate on its axis [O.E. *daeg*, day]
    gaseous: composed of substances that are neither solid nor liquid [Gk. *chaos*, chaos]
    rotation: to turn in a circular motion on an axis [L. *rota*, a wheel]
    terrestrial: earth-like [L. *terra*, the earth]
    year: the length of time it takes a planet to orbit around the sun [O.E. *gear*, year]

INTRODUCTION and ACTIVITY: What makes a "day?" What makes a "night?" Let's find out with an activity. A planet is **rotating** or turning in two directions at the same time. It spins like a top on its **axis**, which is an imaginary line through the middle from the top to the bottom. This is what causes day and night. It is also revolving in a large orbit (or circle) around the sun. One complete time around the sun is a year. How many times have you been around the sun? [*The same number of times as your age.*] Let's spin a top *(or a hard-boiled egg)* and watch how it spins around on its axis and at the same time goes around in a larger circle. This is a picture of what is happening with the earth.

Now let's act out what is happening. I will be the sun and you will spin in a small circle near me to show "day and night." Every time your face is toward me, it is "day". When your back is toward me, it is "night." While you keep spinning, walk in a large circle (orbit) around me. One time all the way around the sun is one year. One little spin represents day and night. *(Several students can participate at the same time if each has a separate "orbit.")*

NOTEBOOK: *Solar System Detective, pp. 19-27. (Work on one or two pages per class period as time allows. If you have a large class, you may wish to make a clear plastic photocopy of the page and fill it out with them on an overhead projector. Another option, especially for younger students, would be to write the answers on the blackboard. The underlined words are the answers.)*

Astronomers from ancient times have observed the planets and charted their courses. Since the 1970's, unmanned space-crafts have provided us with detailed information about each of them. However, much of the information is incomplete and as more discoveries are made, ideas that were once considered to be "facts" often need to be changed.

Because each planet in our solar system has distinctive characteristics that make it different from all the others, you will be filling out a separate *Solar System Detective* page for each one. As I read to you about each planet, listen for the information to mark on your paper.

Let's look over the page before we begin so you will understand what to do. When we talk about a planet's position relative to the sun, we are talking about whether it comes first, second, third and so forth. We describe the distance from the sun with a measurement known as the "**AU**" or "astronomical unit". One AU is equal to the distance from the sun to Earth (approximately 93,000,000 miles). Indicate how far each planet is from the sun by coloring in one space for each AU on the right side of your paper. There are two planets closer to the sun than Earth is, so for them you will only color in 1/3 or 2/3 of the first space, since one space is the distance that Earth is from the sun. There are two main types of planets. One type is a rocky, solid planet called a **terrestrial** (or "earth-like") planet. The other type is gaseous made up mostly of the same types of gases that form the stars. If one of these planets (Jupiter) was 80 times larger, it would be hot enough to ignite into a star. This type of planet is called a **gaseous** planet. Next fill in the length of the day and year. Remember from the activity, a **day** is the period of time it takes a planet spin once on its axis. A **year** is the time that it takes to make one orbit around the sun. Listen closely as I read the information that you will need to fill in each category. I will pause after each piece of information that you need to fill in on the *Solar System Detective* page. I will be happy to repeat anything you need to hear again.

MERCURY: *(Spell the name aloud for student to write on page. Have student look on notebook page 13 to see how the planet looks and how to color it.)* Mercury is the first planet from the sun. *(pause)* It is only about 1/3 *(or .38)* of the distance from the sun that Earth is. *(pause)* It is a dusty, waterless, barren planet scarred with craters by the many meteors that have crashed into it over the years. *(pause)* Mercury is a terrestrial planet with an iron center. It has no gases around it at all, which means it has no atmosphere. *(pause)* Mercury is one third the size of Earth. It is 3,030 miles in diameter. *(pause)* Because it is small in size, its gravity is not as strong as that on Earth. That is why, if you weighed 100 pounds on Earth, you would weigh only 38 pounds on Mercury. *(pause)* It takes 88 days for Mercury to circle the sun. That means that one year on Mercury takes only 88 Earth days. *(pause)* One day on this planet lasts 59 of our days. That makes for very long, extremely hot days and very long, extremely cold nights. *(pause)*

VENUS: *(Spell the name aloud for student to write on page. Have student look on notebook page 13 to see how the planet looks and how to color it.)* Venus is the second planet from the sun. *(pause)* It is covered by clouds of yellow sulfur that rain sulfuric acid. Sulfur is a substance that smells like rotten eggs. No wonder nothing can live there! It is extremely hot—around 900°F (470°C), because the clouds trap in heat. *(pause)* Since this is the closest planet to us, we have sent more space-crafts to it than to any other planet. More than nineteen unmanned space-crafts have gone to this terrestrial planet. *(pause)* The air pressure is 100 times the pressure it is on the earth and some of the space-crafts were crushed. We have learned from these investigations that Venus is a planet with at least one enormous volcano. It is 2/3 *(or .72)* the distance earth is from the sun. *(pause)* It is almost the same size as the earth is. It is 7,520 miles in diameter. *(pause)* For every hundred pounds you weigh on Earth, you would weigh 91 on Venus. *(pause)* A year is 225 earth days. *(pause)* And its day is 243 earth days long. That makes its day longer than its year. *(pause)*

EARTH: *(Spell the name aloud for student to write on page. Have student look on notebook page 13 to see how the planet looks and how to color it.)* The third planet from the sun is Earth. *(pause)* It is the only planet that is capable of supporting plant, animal and human life. *(pause)* Its gravity holds a huge mass of air around it which is called the atmosphere. Earth is a terrestrial planet. *(pause)* The distance from Earth to the sun is the standard we use to describe the relative distance of all the planets. So Earth is 1 AU (astronomical unit) from the sun. *(pause)* Earth is one of the smaller planets in size and is about 7,930 miles in diameter. *(pause)* Since Earth is also our standard basis for weight and time, the weight of the boy would be one hundred pounds *(pause)*, the year is equal to one year *(or 365 1/4 days) (pause)* and the day is equal to 24 hours *(however, the "sidereal day," based on the earth's rotation equals 23 hours, 56 minutes and 4.1 seconds). (pause)* Earth has one moon. This moon has no air, no water, no plants, no animals and no weather. Men have walked on the moon in special space suits and learned a lot about it. We'll be studying much more about Earth later.

MARS: *(Spell the name aloud for student to write on page. Have student look on notebook page 13 to see how the planet looks and how to color it.)* Mars is the fourth planet from the sun. *(pause)* It is 1 1/2 AU's (or 1.52) from the sun. *(pause)* For centuries men have described Mars as the red planet and have wondered whether there might be life on this planet. The red color and ice caps on its north and south poles make Mars distinctive. *(pause)* Through information from unmanned space-crafts, we have been able to learn more about Mars than any other planet. We have learned that it has an atmosphere of 95% carbon dioxide which would cause our blood to boil if we were to land on Mars. Mars is a terrestrial planet and has deserts with wild dust storms, deep canyons that were once thought to be canals dug by Martians, and a volcano 17 miles high named Olympus Mons. *(pause)* It is about half the size of earth. It is 4,220 miles in diameter. *(pause)* For every hundred pounds you weigh on Earth, you would weigh 38 on Mars. *(pause)* A year there is almost twice as long as ours and is 687 earth days. *(pause)* And its day is 24 hours and 37 minutes long. *(pause)*

JUPITER: *(Spell the name aloud for student to write on page. Have student look on notebook page 13 to see how the planet looks and how to color it.)* Jupiter is the fifth planet from the sun. *(pause)* From Jupiter, the sun appears as only a faint flickering star. Jupiter is the largest planet and 1,300 Earths could fit in it. It is 89,000 miles in diameter. *(pause)* Jupiter is a gaseous planet, with very volatile gasses *(hydrogen, helium, methane, ammonia and water vapor)* and it is the only planet to give off more heat than it gets from the sun. *(pause)* It may have a rocky core where temperatures are estimated to be 53,000 degrees Fahrenheit. A distinctive feature of Jupiter is the Great Red Spot. *(pause)* It appears to be a tremendous storm in Jupiter's atmosphere with hurricane-like winds that rage at 300 miles per hour. This storm is larger than three Earths in size and travels around the planet every six days. This storm has been going on for more than 300 years. Jupiter shines brightly and has rings of rocks orbiting it and at least 16 moons. It is 5 1/4 AU's *(or 5.2)* from the sun. *(pause)* For every hundred pounds you weigh on Earth, you would weigh 234 on Jupiter. *(pause)* A year is 11.8 earth years. *(pause)* And its day is 9 hours and 51 earth minutes long. *(pause)*

SATURN: *(Spell the name aloud for student to write on page. Have student look on notebook page 13 to see how the planet looks and how to color it.)* Saturn is the sixth planet from the sun. *(pause)* One of the most distinctive things about Saturn is its colorful rings that are visible with even a small telescope. The rings appear to be pieces of rocks, dust and ice. *(pause)* Saturn is 9 1/2 AU's *(or 9.54)* from the sun. *(pause)* Saturn measures 75,000 miles in diameter. *(pause)* It is a gaseous planet with large storms and strong winds. *(pause)* Saturn has a strong magnetic field around it. For every hundred pounds you weigh on Earth, you would weigh 93 on Saturn. *(pause)* A year is 29.4 earth years. *(pause)* It is spinning very fast and its day is 10 hours and 15 earth minutes long. *(pause)*

URANUS: *(Spell the name aloud for student to write on page. Have student look on notebook page 13 to see how the planet looks and how to color it.)* Uranus (YOUR-uh-nus) is the seventh planet from the sun. *(pause)* It is 19 1/5 AU's *(or 19.19)* from the sun. *(pause)* Uranus is another gaseous planet. *(pause)* It appears to have an icy, blue-green appearance. *(pause)* Uranus is 32,200 miles in diameter. *(pause)* For every hundred pounds you weigh on Earth, you would weigh 85 on Uranus. *(pause)* A year is 84 earth years. *(pause)* Pluto and Uranus are the only planets that spin on an axis that is on the same level as their orbit. This means that their poles (instead of their equators) face the sun. It has rings similar to Saturn, but they are much smaller and fainter. And Uranus' day is 17 hours and 12 earth minutes long. *(pause)*

NEPTUNE: *(Spell the name aloud for student to write on page. Have student look on notebook page 13 to see how the planet looks and how to color it.)* Neptune is the eighth planet from the sun. It is 30 AU's *(or 30.07)* from the sun. *(pause)* Neptune is a gaseous planet. *(pause)*

Temperatures on Neptune are very cold *(within 60 degrees Celsius of absolute zero)* and it has tremendous windstorms on its surface. It has a perpetual storm, called the Great Dark Spot, *(pause)* that is about the size of the earth. Neptune has a diameter of 30,800 miles. *(pause)* For every hundred pounds you weigh on Earth you would weigh 114 on Neptune. *(pause)* A year is 164.8 earth years. *(pause)* And its day is 17 hours and 50 earth minutes long. *(pause)*

PLUTO: *(Spell the name aloud for student to write on page. Have student look on notebook page 13 to see how the planet looks and how to color it.)* Pluto is the ninth planet from the sun. *(pause)* Because of its elliptical orbit, it was closer to the sun than Neptune from 1989 to 1999. Its average distance from the sun is 39 1/2 AU's. *(pause)* It is a very small planet, only 1,620 miles in diameter. *(pause)* It was discovered in 1930, making it the most recent planet to be discovered. *(pause)* Because it is so far away, little is known about Pluto. It is believed to be an icy terrestrial type planet. *(pause)* For every hundred pounds you weigh on Earth, you would weigh 4 pounds on Pluto. *(pause)* A year is 248.4 earth years. *(pause)* And its day is 6 earth days and 9 hours long. *(pause)*

(Use this chart for checking the information on the Solar Detective pages.)

Planet	Position from sun	Distance from sun (Earth to sun=AU)	Distinctive features:	Size (diameter in miles)	Type of planet	Weight: 100# on Earth =	Year (by Earth time)	Day (by Earth time)
Mercury	1st	1/3 AU (.38)	Barren craters	3,030	Terrestrial	38 #	88 days	59 days
Venus	2nd	2/3 AU (.72)	Yellow sulfur gas	7,520	Terrestrial	91 #	225 days	243 days
Earth	3rd	1.00 AU	Life	7,930	Terrestrial	100 #	1 year (365 1/4 days)	24 hrs (23 hrs., 56 min., 4.1 sec.)
Mars	4th	1 1/2 AU (1.52)	Red with ice caps	4,220	Terrestrial	38 #	687 days	24 hrs., 37 min.
Jupiter	5th	5 1/4 AU (5.20)	Great Red Spot	89,000	Gaseous	234 #	11.8 years	9 hrs., 51 min.
Saturn	6th	9 1/2 AU (9.54)	Colorful rings	75,000	Gaseous	93 #	29.4 years	10 hrs., 15 min.
Uranus	7th	19 1/5 AU (19.19)	Icy blue-green	32,200	Gaseous	85 #	84 years	17 hrs 12 min.
Neptune	8th	30 AU (30.07)	Great Dark Spot	30,800	Gaseous	114 #	164.8 years	17 hrs., 50 min.
Pluto	9th	39 1/2 AU (average)	Recent discovery	1,620	Terrestrial	4 #	248.4 years	6 days, 9 hrs.

REVIEW: 1. How many planets are there in our solar system? [*nine*]
2. Name them in the order of their position from the sun. [*Mercury, Venus, Earth, Mars, Jupiter, Saturn, Uranus, Neptune, Pluto*]
3. Which planet is the only planet that supports life? [*Earth*]
4. Which planets have orbits that over-lap? [*Neptune and Pluto*]

5. What does "orbit" mean? [*the path of a heavenly body as it rotates around another body*]
6. What is "gravity"? [*the force that attracts one object to another, as the pull of the sun on the earth*]

TEST: *Student will need* **notebook p. 245,** *Crossword Review 1. Use as a review or test for older students.* **Answers:** *Teacher's p. 123.*

Have the student explain his notebook page to a friend or relative and tell what he learned from the lesson.

DIGGING DEEPER: 1. Take an imaginary space tour of at least two planets and write a letter home to tell about what you have seen. 2. Visit a planetarium. 3. Read a biography of a famous astronomer, such as Nicolaus Copernicus (1473–1543), Johannes Kepler (1571–1630), Galileo Galilei (1564–1642), or Caroline Lucretia Herschel (1750-1848) and fill out a *Scientist Detective* page. 4. Research the meaning of the names of all the planets. (*Remembering God's Awesome Acts, pp. 240-242* by Susan Mortimer, can help you get started with this.) 5. There is the possibility of a tenth planet that has not yet been discovered. What would you name it and how would you look for it? 6. Study the difference between "gradualism" and "planetary catastrophism" in the field of "cosmology" (the study of past conditions of the solar system). 7. Summarize, in an outline form, the preparation and requirements needed to become an astronaut.

THE EARTH

LESSON 5: Our Planet Earth

Our Planet Earth *will be covered in three separate lessons. But first, do the notebook page,* The Earth. *It will be needed to provide the illustrations for the material to be covered in each lesson.*

PREPARATION: *Student will need* **notebook pp. 28-30,** *scissors, glue, and crayons.*

NOTEBOOK: *The Earth, pp. 28-30.* Let's cut out the layers of the earth from *The Earth (page 2).* Then glue the circles of the Earth's layers onto *The Earth* page. Glue on the circle marked "C" first, then "B", and last, "A". Cut out the pieces from *The Earth (page 2)* to glue onto the Earth's Atmosphere section on *The Earth* page.

If it were not for the atmosphere, we wouldn't have blue skies, pretty sunsets, or beautiful rainbows. And with the rainbow is the special promise that God will never destroy the earth again by a flood. A rainbow is made when droplets of water bend waves of light and reflect different colors. Let's make a pop-out rainbow for *The Earth* page. Color the rainbow on *The Earth (page 2)* the correct colors. Each word on the rainbow begins with the same letter as the color that should be used for that line. *(e.g.,* **Rainbow** *=* **Red,** **Over** *=* **Orange,** *and so forth.)* Next cut out the rainbow and the rainbow square to glue on *The Earth* page. Glue the circle on the blank front cover of the square.

SONG/POEM: The words on the pop-out rainbow you made will help you learn the colors of the rainbow and remind you of the story of Noah. The rainbow was a sign of God's promise that He would never flood the earth again. Let's read Genesis 9:9–16 together. The first line of the poem will help you to remember the order of the colors in the rainbow. Each word begins with the same letter as the color it represents.

> **Rainbows Over You**
> **R**ainbows **O**ver **Y**ou, God's Blessed Vow,
> That He will never flood the earth again.
> **R**ainbows **O**ver **Y**ou, God's Blessed Vow,
> And to His Word, our God is always true.
>
> **R**ainbows **O**ver **Y**ou, **R**ed, **O**range, **Y**ellow,
> The colors in the sky tell of God's care.
> **G**od's **B**lessed **V**ow, **G**reen, **B**lue, **V**iolet,
> They promise that our God is always there.

EVOLUTION STUMPERS: Over 200 different cultures from around the world have original accounts of a worldwide flood. How could so many have similar stories if such a flood didn't really happen?

Lesson 5:A Light

PREPARATION: *You will need a sunny day, a flashlight (or a candle and matches), a lamp, a shallow pan filled with water, a mirror, and a piece of white paper.*

INTRODUCTION and ACTIVITY: Can you imagine living without light? There was a time when there was no light. The Bible tells us that in the beginning the earth was empty and without anything. Then on the first day of creation, God created the light and dark. He called the light "day," and the dark He called "night," and He was pleased.

Now, I am going to let you see some different kinds of light. *(Turn off the electric light and darken the room. Then light a candle or turn on a flashlight.)* Can you think of a brighter light that helps us see? *(Go out into the sunshine.)* If we took the flashlight outside into the sunshine, we would hardly notice the light from it because the light from the sun is so strong. That is the same reason why we don't notice the stars when the sun is shining. The stars are out there, but the sun makes it too bright for us to see them.

Light from the sun appears to be white. But it is really made up of all the colors in the rainbow. Some colors we can't see with our eyes. The color waves we can see are red, orange, yellow, green, blue, and violet. When we see a red flower, what is actually happening is that light from the sun with all its colors hits the flower; the flower absorbs all the colors but red, which bounces off into our eyes, and we see red.

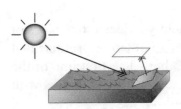

Look at the rainbow on your notebook page. A rainbow is a beautiful example of how light waves are bent. Let's make a rainbow. Place a pan of water in a sunny spot. Lean a mirror into the water at an angle that catches the reflection of the sun below the level of the water. Hold up a piece of white paper to catch the reflected light. You will have a vivid rainbow on the paper!

BIBLE READING: *(Have student look up Scriptures.)* Jesus is called the Light of the World (John 1:1–5). Why would He be like light to us? He leads us so we can see where to go without getting hurt (Psalm 119:105; John 8:12). He keeps us warm and safe with His love. He gives us life. Darkness is the absence of light. God planned darkness for the night so that we could have a time of rest and refreshment.

Some people think that they can hide in the darkness, so they do bad things in the dark (Proverbs 4:18–19; 1 Thessalonians 5:5). But to God, darkness and light are the same (Psalm 139:11–12). He can see even when we can't. And while we are asleep, He is always awake, watching and protecting us (Psalm 121:4–8, 139:17–18). God wants us to be like lights, or goodness, in the dark and evil world around us (1 John 1:5–9; Ephesians 5:8).

Lesson 5:B The Earth

PREPARATION: *You will need a hard boiled egg, a small, narrow glass, a sandbox (optional), a bottle of vinegar, 2-3 tablespoons of baking soda, and red food coloring. Vocabulary words may be written on flash cards.*

VOCABULARY:

> **biosphere:** layer of earth that supports life, including land, sea, and air [Gk. *bios*, life + *sphaira*, a globe, circle. Biosphere = circle of life.]
> **core:** the center of the earth, consisting of molten ore [L. *cor*, the heart]
> **crust** : hard, outer covering of the earth—4 to 22 miles thick [L. *crusta*, covering]
> **earthquake:** movement in the earth's crust [O.E. *erothe*, earth + *cwacian*, to shake]
> **mantle:** the middle layer of the earth [L. *mantellum*, a cloak, covering]
> **volcano:** an opening in the earth through which gases, ash, and lava are ejected
> [L. *Vulcanus*, the god of fire]

INTRODUCTION and ACTIVITY: Let's look at the layers of the earth on your notebook page, *The Earth*. We often think of the earth as being a solid ball. In fact, it is neither solid nor is it a true sphere (ball shaped), but an ellipsoid (oval shaped). The earth's center is a fiery hot melted ball with only a very thin outer crust covering it. The earth is flatter at both poles and wider at the equator. If it were possible to drive straight through the middle of the earth at 60 miles per hour, it would take us about 132 hours. That would be just a little less than 6 days, driving day and night!

Our earth is made up of many layers. Let's start with the part of the earth we live on. This part of the earth is the only part that can support life. It is called the **biosphere** and includes the land, sea, and air. Even though we call the planet "Earth", there is more water than land on the earth's surface. In fact, more than 71% of the earth's surface is covered with water. If you took all the water away, you would see that the land under the ocean is very much like the rest of the land. Earth is considered a "terrestrial planet", which means that it is basically a solid planet and not a gaseous one. There are valleys and mountains, and in fact, islands are the tops of tall ocean mountains. Let's take a hard boiled egg and cut it in half lengthwise *(leave shell on)*. The egg will help us visualize the layers of the earth. The shell of the egg is like the crust of the earth. The earth's **crust** is actually a very narrow layer, only 4–22 miles in depth, which is even thinner by comparison than the shell is in proportion to the egg. This "shell", or crust on the earth, is broken into plates that are in motion, carrying the continents on top of them. Where these broken plates collide, there are lots of **earthquakes** and the earth is folded into mountains. Hot melted (molten) rock called "lava", spews out of **volcanoes**. This leads us to the question: Where does all that hot molten rock come from? It comes from the **upper mantle** and the **lower mantle** of the earth. These layers are represented by the white layer of the egg. The mantle is about 1,780 miles deep and is made up of molten rock. The yolk (or yellow) of the egg represents the **core** of the earth, which again has two parts. The **outer core** is made of melted (or molten) iron. It is about 1,300 miles deep. Finally, the **inner core** consists of mostly iron and nickel and is nearly a solid ball because of the tremendous pressure on it. The temperatures here are very, very hot, reaching up to 11,000 degrees Fahrenheit. This is almost the same temperature as that of the surface of the sun.

Let's make a "volcano". First we will put a small glass in the sand and form the sand around it to look like a volcano. *(If no sand is available, put the glass in a pan or do the activity outside.)* Now we will fill the glass half full of vinegar. We can add red food coloring to make it look like "lava." Next, sprinkle baking soda into the vinegar and watch what happens. *(Keep adding baking soda until the "volcano" stops foaming.)* The force that caused our "volcano" to "erupt" was a chemical one. The force that causes real volcanoes to erupt is the tremendous build up of pressure inside the earth's mantle.

BIBLE READING: *(Have student look up Scriptures.)* We often think of the earth as being a solid place. Most of the time it is. But some of us have felt the earth move in little and big earthquakes. And Jesus told us that before He returned, there would be wars, big earthquakes, plagues, famines and great signs in the sun, moon and stars (Matthew 24:3–7, 29–31; Mark 13:8; Luke 21:11, 25–36). But He also has promised faithfully that He will be with us, even to the end of the age (Matthew 28:18–20). We also know that God is our refuge and strength, so we do not need to fear, even if the earth quakes and the mountains fall into the sea (Psalm 46:1–3). God tells us over 450 times in the Bible not to fear (Psalm 112:1, 6–8; Matthew 6:33–34; 2 Timothy 1:7). And we know that nothing can separate us from God's love—not death, nor life, nor anything else in the whole world (Romans 8:31, 32, 38, 39). So when you hear of bad things happening, don't be afraid. These things are signs that Jesus is coming back to be with those who truly love Him. Come quickly, Lord Jesus! (Revelation 22:7, 20)

DIGGING DEEPER: 1. Watch the video, *Thundering Earth*, from Moody Institute of Science, 820 N. La Salle Blvd, Chicago, IL, 60610, 1995. 2. Read the section on "Planet Earth" in the *Usborne Encyclopedia of Planet Earth*, EDC PUBLISHING, 10302 E. 55th Place, Tulsa, OK, 74146. (Usborne books do have evolutionary references, but these can provide opportunity for discussion of creation.)

Lesson 5:C The Atmosphere

PREPARATION: *Vocabulary words may be written on flash cards.*

VOCABULARY:
> **atmosphere:** the blanket of air surrounding a heavenly body [Gk. *atmos*, vapor]
> **exosphere:** the outer-most layer of atmosphere [Gk. *exo*, outside]
> **mesosphere:** the cold middle layer of air [Gk. *mesos*, middle]
> **ozone layer:** a protective layer of condensed oxygen, O_3 (which has a peculiar smell) in the stratosphere [Gk. *ozein*, to smell]
> **sphere:** globe [Gk. *sphaira*, a globe]
> **stratosphere:** the second layer of air above the earth's surface [L. *stratum*, layer]
> **thermosphere:** the upper layer of thin air which contains many electrically charged atoms and where temperatures increase with altitude [Gk. *thermos*, heat]
> **troposphere:** the layer of air closest to the earth's surface [Gk. *tropos*, a turn]

INTRODUCTION: Let's look at the layers of the atmosphere on your notebook page, *The Earth*. I will be asking you questions that you can figure out by looking at the page. The **atmosphere** is the blanket of air wrapped around the earth, held in place by gravity. It is divided into five main layers. What is the first 10 miles up called? [*the troposphere*] The **troposphere** contains the oxygen that we need to breathe, the carbon dioxide that plants need, and the water vapor that every living thing needs. Where does most of what we know as "weather" such as clouds, wind and rain occur? [*the troposphere*] Breathing becomes increasingly difficult when you go up more than two miles above sea level because the concentration of oxygen becomes less the higher you go. In which layer do jet planes fly? [*the troposphere*]

The next layer is the **stratosphere**, which includes the area from 10 to 30 miles above the earth's surface. In which layer is the ozone located? [*the stratosphere*] The stratosphere contains the warm **ozone layer** which is strongest between 12 and 24 miles high. Look carefully at the ozone layer and tell me what is stopped by the ozone layer? [*The protective ozone layer keeps harmful rays and much of the ultraviolet light of the sun from reaching the earth. Most meteorites do not reach land because they burn up when they hit the ozone layer.*] From what you may have heard in the news, do you know what is causing holes in the ozone? [*It is being broken down by natural causes as well as air pollution.*] Without ozone protection, more ultraviolet light reaches the earth, and the dangers of skin cancer and eye problems are greatly increased. Also, the growth of plants is affected.

What is the layer above the stratosphere? [*the mesosphere*] The **mesosphere** is the layer from 30 to 50 miles above ground level. Temperatures get colder the higher the altitude. What layer is above the mesosphere? [*the thermosphere*] Temperatures again get hotter as the altitude increases in the **thermosphere**, but since the air is very thin, it does not actually feel very hot. This layer contains tiny electrically charged particles that reflect radio waves and make long-distance communication possible. It is the level at which the external tanks separate from the space shuttle. What glows with vivid colors at times in the thermosphere? [*the Aurora Polaris, the beautiful northern (aurora borealis) and southern (aurora australis) lights*]

What is the last layer of earth's atmosphere? [*the exosphere*] The **exosphere** begins about 350 miles above the earth and has no clear ending point. The air there gets thinner and thinner until it reaches the vacuum of space.

BIBLE READING: *(Have student look up Scriptures.)* When you look up into the sky, you can't see the end of it. If you got into a space ship, you could reach the edge of the earth's atmosphere. However you could travel and travel and never reach the end of the heavens. The Psalms tell us that as high as the heavens are above the earth, so great is God's love and kindness (Psalm 103:11). If you keep traveling to the east, you will never ever reach the west. And that is how far God has removed our sins from us (Psalm 103:12). We can surely trust a God who is as loving and forgiving as this!

REVIEW: 1. Name the colors of the rainbow in order. [*red, orange, yellow, green, blue, violet*]
2. What is the outside layer of the earth called and how thick is it? [*crust; 19 to 22 miles thick*]
3. Where is the mantle of the earth? [*it is the middle layer of the earth*]
4. What is the core of the earth made of? [*the center of the earth consists of molten ore*]
5. What is the atmosphere? [*the blanket of air surrounding a heavenly body*]
6. Which layer of the atmosphere contains the ozone layer? [*stratosphere*]

TEST: *Student will need* **notebook p. 246,** *Crossword Review 2. Use as a review or test for older students.* **Answers:** *Teacher's p. 123.*

Have the student explain his notebook page to a friend or relative and tell what he learned from the lesson.

DIGGING DEEPER: 1. Research the saltwater bodies of the earth (oceans and seas). [The oceans are the Pacific (63.8 million sq. mi.), the Atlantic (31.8 million sq. mi.), the Indian (28.4 million sq. mi.) and the Arctic (5.4 million sq. mi.)] 2. Study the continents—names, locations, highest mountains, longest rivers, and so forth. Make a relief map of land formations with salt and flour dough. Mix equal parts salt and flour and add enough water to make a smooth dough. Food coloring may be added. Dry in the oven or in the sun. [The continents are Europe, Asia (check out "Eurasia"), Africa, North and South America, Australia, and Antarctica.] 3. Follow a mission of the space program, either on television or newspaper, and watch for aspects that relate to the atmosphere. 4. Watch the video, *Roaring Waters*, from Moody Institute of Science, 820 N. La Salle Blvd, Chicago, IL, 60610, 1995. 5. Learn more about Earth's moon. (A good resource is: *Our Created Moon: Earth's Fascinating Neighbor* by Don B. DeYoung, Master Books, P. O. Box 727, Green Forest, AR, 72638, 2003.)

NON-LIVING THINGS: ROCKS and MINERALS

LESSON 6: Rocks

Rocks will be covered in three lessons.

Lesson 6:A Igneous rock

PREPARATION: *You will need an eggbeater, a mixing bowl, and one egg white. Vocabulary words may be written on flash cards.*

VOCABULARY:

> **crystalline**: mineral body (like quartz) with regular geometric shapes [Gk. *kruos*, frost]
> **extrusive:** refers to igneous rock formed when magma cools above the surface of the earth [L. *ex*, out; *trudere*, to thrust]
> **igneous rock:** rock formed as a result of intense heat [L. *ignis*, fire]
> **intrusive:** refers to igneous rock formed when magma cools below the surface of the earth [L. *in*, within + *trudere*, to thrust]
> **magma:** hot, molten (melted) rock [Gk. *magma*, to knead]

INTRODUCTION and ACTIVITY: The outer crust of our earth consists primarily of rock. Rock gives shape and substance to our planet and provides many useful products for us. What are some things that we build with rocks? [*We use rocks for building roads and fences. Rocks are also used in making concrete that provides a solid foundation for building a house.*] Where do metals come from? [*We get metals such as copper, silver, gold and iron from rocks.*] What are metals used for? [*for cars, silverware, and thousands of other products*] What do we use precious stones for? [*We decorate ourselves with diamonds, rubies and other precious stones in jewelry and watches.*]

There are three basic groups of rocks on our planet. **Igneous** rock is formed deep beneath the earth's surface from **magma**, or hot molten rock, that is rich in minerals and gases. "Igneous" comes from a word that means "fire." The word "ignite", which means "to set on fire", may help you remember this type of rock. There are two types of igneous rock. If the magma cools slowly beneath the earth's surface, it forms large **crystalline** rocks, that is, rocks with tightly packed crystals of quartz. An example of this type of **intrusive** rock is granite. In a piece of granite you can see crystals of quartz, feldspar and biotite mica.

Sometimes the magma is forced up through the crust of the earth and spills out on the surface as when a volcano erupts. The magma, now called lava, cools rapidly on the surface of the earth, and forms extremely different types of rocks called **extrusive** rocks. Two of these are obsidian and pumice. Obsidian is a smooth, black natural glass. In the past it was often used to make arrowheads. Pumice has gas bubbles trapped in it. It is very lightweight in proportion to its size, and has a rough, sponge-like appearance. Large pieces of this rock can be seen floating on the surface of lakes and rivers that are near volcanoes. Pumice rock is also used in saunas and barbecue grills because it retains heat well. The amazing thing about the glassy black obsidian and the bubble-filled pumice is that they are chemically the same and yet they look so different.

Let's illustrate this with an egg white. Do you see how glassy the egg white looks? Now we will beat it into a thick meringue. How does the meringue differ from the egg white before it was whipped? [*bigger, larger volume for the same weight; can't see through it*] This is similar to the differences between obsidian and pumice. Obsidian is rock without gas bubbles. Pumice is like whipped rock, full of gas bubbles.

BIBLE READING: *(Have student look up Scriptures.)* Some rocks contain a mineral called ore. Certain metals come from ore, but the ore must be melted down (refined) before the metal can be shaped into usable objects. Two of these rare and precious metals are gold and silver. The Bible has a lot to say about them (Genesis 13:2, 23:15–16; Job 28:1–6). Gold was one of the gifts given to Jesus by the wise men at His birth (Matthew 2:11), and it was for thirty pieces of silver that Judas betrayed Jesus (Matthew 26:15). Jesus told us not to try to get rich with things like gold and silver, but to put our efforts into heavenly treasures (Matthew 6:19–21, 10:9). One of these heavenly treasures is God's word. It is more precious than gold (Psalm 12:6, 19:10; Proverbs 8:19). The power of Jesus in us can't be bought with silver or gold (Act 3:6, 8:18–24). The process of becoming more like Jesus Christ in our lives is like the refining process that metals go through to become pure and valuable (1 Peter 1:7; Revelation 3:18).

DIGGING DEEPER: 1. Watch the video, *Hidden Treasure*, from Moody Institute of Science, 820 N. La Salle Blvd, Chicago, IL, 60610, 1995. 2. Visit a museum of natural history and look at the rock and mineral displays. 3. Study *Creation Geology: A Study Guide to Fossils, Formations and the Flood!* by Felice Gerwitz & Jill Whitlock, Media Angels, 15720 S. Pebble Lane, Fort Myers, FL, 33912-2341.

Lesson 6:B Sedimentary and Metamorphic Rock

PREPARATION: *You will need a sugar cookie dough or salt/flour dough (1 cup flour to 1 cup salt with enough water to make a pliable dough), cookie sheets, and an oven. Optional items include: a piece of "green ware", pottery glaze, a kiln, or any fine china object. Student will need notebook pp. 31, 33-34, scissors, crayons, and glue. Vocabulary words may be written on flash cards.*

VOCABULARY:
> **erosion:** to wear away or break down into small pieces [L. *erodere*, to wear away]
> **fossil:** any evidence of life from the past [L. *fossum*, to dig]
> **metamorphic rock:** rock which has been changed by heat and pressure
> [Gk. *meta*, over + *morphe*, shape]
> **sedimentary rock:** rock made up of layers of materials settled underwater
> [L. *sedere*, to settle]

INTRODUCTION and ACTIVITY: Over time, rocks wear down into smaller rocks, pebbles and sand. This process is called **erosion**. Water and wind are the primary forces that break down any kind of rock into tiny pieces. **Sedimentary** (which means "to settle") rock is formed when tiny pieces of rock along with plant and animal remains, are deposited in layers under water. They become cemented together into rock. Examples of this kind of rock include sandstone and shale. Sedimentary rock is the only kind of rock that contains **fossils**. Fossils are any evidence of life from the past. Some of the fossils that are found in sedimentary rock include imprints of animal feet and leaf prints as well as shells, bones and wood. When the mud or sand hardens around the different objects, it forms a mold of them. Over the years, the wood, plants, shell and bone material slowly rot or erode away. Minerals fill in the space, taking on the same shape and structure. So petrified wood is not really wood that turned to stone, but is the result of wood slowly eroding and being replaced with minerals that have taken on the exact shape and structure in rock.

(Get out either sugar cookie dough or salt/flour dough and give each child a large piece. Have a floured or plastic wrap work surface prepared. Preheat oven.) Let's pretend to make a fossil imprint on this piece of dough. Flatten the dough by pressing it with your hand. What design do you see on the dough? *[hand print—you may also let the child try pressing other objects into the dough]* Now let's put our "rock" on the cookie sheet and bake it. When we cook our "rock", our "fossil" imprint will remain.

Both igneous rocks and sedimentary rocks can be changed when they are exposed to extreme heat and pressure. These are then known as **metamorphic** rocks, or "changed rock." Heat and pressure can come from several sources: The first is close contact with volcanic activity. The second is the friction of two folds of land that are rubbing and pushing each other. The third is a result of more and more rocks piling up, causing heat and a lot of pressure on the rocks underneath. The changes may be great or small. One example is limestone turning into marble under heat and pressure. Another example is graphite (the black center part of your pencil) becoming an artificial type of diamond. If metamorphic rocks are exposed to extreme heat, they are melted to become the magma that forms igneous rocks. This cycle of rock formation is shown on the *Rock Cycle* page of your notebook.

(Optional activity: Make some pottery, or show student a piece of fine china that has already been fired and discuss the following steps. Get a piece of green ware, clean, glaze, and fire it. Talk about how soft the green ware was. It was made out of clay that could easily be carved or broken. With heat, the clay became hard and the glazes turned into glass and changed color.)

BIBLE READING: *(Have student look up Scriptures.)* Rocks are the firm foundation of our earth. Jesus tells the story of a wise man who built his house on a rock and it stood firm in spite of floods (Luke 6:46–49). Jesus, in fact, is likened to a rock (Psalms 18:1–3; 1 Peter 2:6–8; Ephesians 2:20). He is indeed the firm foundation not only of our physical earth, but also of our spiritual world. You and I are told to be like living stones, to build a spiritual house of worship for Jesus (1 Peter 2:4–6). What God desires as our spiritual worship is not just a sacrifice but obedience to His commandments (1 Samuel 15:22). Jesus summed up all of the commandments into two: Love God with all your being and love your neighbor as yourself (Mark 12:28–34).

NOTEBOOK: *The Rock Cycle, pp. 31, 33-34.* Color and cut out the little pages on the *Rock Cycle (page 2)*. These pages will be glued (in reverse order) on the *Rock Cycle* page. On 1a, color the magma red. On 3a, for a shiny glaze, coat the picture of obsidian with a liquid glue or clear fingernail polish. Allow time for this to dry before gluing first 2a then 1a in place. On 2b, glue sand or salt on the picture of the sandstone. On 3b, choose a fossil to draw on the limestone. On 1c, color all the areas where you would find metamorphic rocks. (This should include the rock formations beside each arrow.) Draw a fossil on the limestone on page 2c. On 3c, color the graphite with your pencil, which is really made with graphite, and then coat the diamond with liquid glue or clear fingernail polish. When you finish, we will read each booklet together aloud.

EVOLUTION STUMPERS: It has been estimated that with erosion and the breakdown of plants, about 6 inches of topsoil is formed over 5–20,000 years. Most of the land on the earth has only 7–8 inches of topsoil. If the earth were millions of years old, as evolutionists say it is, shouldn't there be a lot more topsoil?

DIGGING DEEPER: 1. Research fossils as they relate to creation science. 2. Explore the Internet for information about rocks, minerals and fossils. 3. Play GeoSafari® Science questions about rocks. (The CD ROM version is great!) 4. Fill out a *Scientist Detective* page for one of these: William Buckland (1784-1856) who identified the first dinosaur; Nicolaus Steno (1638-1686), geologist; George Cuvier (1769-1832) paleontologist; Louis Leakey (1903-1972), son of a missionary, whose fossil discoveries in Africa advanced the cause for human evolution. 5. Read *The Geology Book* by Dr. John D. Morris, Master Books, Green Forest, AR, 2000. 6. Check out the website: www.answersingenesis.org. While there, listen to Buddy Davis sing, "Billions of Dead Things." 7. Enjoy the *Truth Seekers* series by Christina and Felice Gerwitz, Media Angels, 15720 S. Pebble Lane, Fort Myers, FL, 33912-2341. (These are novels about homeschooled teen paleontologists who encounter adventure as they look for evidence to support creationism.)

Lesson 6:C Becoming a Rock Detective

PREPARATION: *You will need a field book on rock classifications, or encyclopedia. Each student will need **notebook pp. 32, 35-37,** several types of small rocks, a penny, a steel nail, a metal file, a permanent ink pen, and an empty egg carton.*

INTRODUCTION and ACTIVITY: *Rock Detective, pp. 32, 35-37.* You will be looking closely at rocks for this lesson. The *Rock Detective* pages will help you learn how to classify and analyze them. Pick several types of rocks to work with. Don't try to fill in the name until the very end.

☑ Look at your first rock. What colors are in it?

☑ Now scratch the rock on a concrete sidewalk or driveway. What color of streak does it leave? Is it a different color than the rock itself?

☑ Next look at the texture. Is the rock smooth with very small or fine particles in it, or is it rough with larger or coarse particles?

☑ What about the weight? Does it feel lighter or heavier than you would expect for a rock of its size?

☑ Does it have a shiny appearance? If so, what kind of shine?

☑ What characteristics does it have? Can it separate into flaky sheets? Does it have holes?

☑ How hard is your rock? The softest rock is talc. Talc is so soft it was used in the past to make baby powder. Diamonds are the hardest rocks, and many others are in-between the two. Try scratching your rock with your fingernail, a penny, and a steel nail. This will help you to determine the hardness of the rock. Mark the number of hardness as the first item that can scratch the rock.

☑ Look at the cleavage of the rock (the direction the rock would split or break). Circle or draw the shape of crystals, if any, that you see in the rock.

☑ Next decide what classification of rock you have (igneous, sedimentary, or metamorphic) and color in the picture of your choice. Using the information you have collected about your rock, look it up in a field guide to rocks and minerals and see if you can figure out its name. (*This may be difficult even with a rock classification book, but make an "educated guess."*) Even if you can't figure out exactly which rock it is, you have learned a lot about it.

Let's do several other rocks in the same way. Later, if you find a rock, you will know how and what to look for. In order to keep track of your rocks and start a rock collection, number the rock with a permanent ink pen and put the matching number on the back of the *Rock Detective* page. If your rocks are small enough, you can store them in an egg carton. You may wish to mix up all the rocks that you have studied and try to match the rock with the *Rock Detective* page that goes with it. (*With more than one student, exchange collections and match each rock to its description.*)

TEST: *Student will need* **notebook p. 247,** *Crossword Review 3. Use as a review or test for older students.* **Answers:** *Teacher's p. 124.*

WEATHER

LESSON 7: Weather

Weather *will be covered in five separate lessons. When they have been completed, do the notebook page,* The Weather Recipe, ***pp. 39, 41-42***.

Lesson 7:A Sun and Weather

PREPARATION: *Copy this weather recipe onto the blackboard:* weather = sun + air + water + rotation & revolution + land. *You will need a flashlight and a large piece of paper. Vocabulary words may be written on flash cards.*

VOCABULARY:
> **climate:** the overall weather pattern of an area [Gk. *klima*, slope]
> **equator:** an imaginary line dividing the earth into the northern and southern
> hemispheres [L. *aequus*, equal]
> **hemisphere:** half of the earth [Gk. *hemi*, half + *sphaira*, a globe]
> **humidity:** how much moisture there is in the air [L. *humidus*, moist]
> **precipitation:** amount of rain or snow [L. *praeceps*, headlong]
> **temperature:** how hot or cold it is [L. *temperare*, to moderate]
> **weather:** the condition of the atmosphere at any given time or place
> [O.E. *weder*, weather]

INTRODUCTION & ACTIVITIES: Many factors work together to cause different **climates** (the over-all weather pattern of an area). **Weather** is the condition of the atmosphere at any given time or place. We describe it by the **temperature** (how hot or cold it is), the **humidity** (how much moisture there is in the air), the **precipitation** (amount of rain or snow), the wind (speed and direction) and how cloudy it is (clear sky or cloudy). Let's look at some of the factors that produce changes in the weather. Here is a "recipe" for weather. What are the ingredients? (weather = sun + air + water + rotation & revolution + land) We will be talking about how each of these affects the weather, but today we will begin with the sun and its effect on the weather.

The sun is one of the ingredients we notice the most. When the sun is shining, the weather is usually warmer than when it is dark or cloudy. The angle at which the sun's rays hit the earth affects the amount of heat that is felt there. Let's try an experiment to show this. First we will lay a large piece of paper on the floor. Now darken the room and point a flashlight straight down on the paper. Look at *(or draw on the paper)* how big the area of light is. The circle of light is very round and quite bright. Now, hold the flashlight horizontally about two inches from the floor so that the light again shines on the paper. Look at *(or draw on the same paper)* the area of light. Notice that the light area covers a larger area but is not as bright and it is more like an oval than a circle. In the same way, when the sun's rays strike the earth at an angle, they provide less heat. It is the angle of the sun's rays, and not how close the sun is, that determines whether it is hot or cold. This angle is what causes the seasonal changes. Even though the earth is miles closer to the sun when it is winter (in the northern hemisphere), the angle of the sun's rays is slanted. This provides less heat, resulting in colder temperatures. The **equator** (an imaginary line dividing the earth into **hemispheres**) receives direct rays all year round. As a result, the temperatures are hotter and there are few seasonal changes.

DIGGING DEEPER: 1. Research and write a report about the seasons in the Northern and Southern hemispheres, at the equator, and at the poles, focusing on the effect of the sun on the weather. 2. Describe the climate of your area and tell what you like and don't like about it.

Lesson 7:B Air and Weather

PREPARATION: *Copy this weather recipe onto the blackboard:* weather = sun + air + water + rotation & revolution + land. *Vocabulary words may be written on flash cards.*

VOCABULARY:
> **molecules**: the smallest piece of any substance that can be identified as that substance [L. *moles*, a mass]
> **vacuum**: vacant or empty space [L. *vacuus*, empty]

INTRODUCTION and ACTIVITY: The air is another important ingredient in our weather recipe. We notice the air when it is moving and call it "wind." Air can be calm or violent. As air warms up, it becomes lighter and rises. Air that gets cold becomes heavier and sinks. The wind is caused by heavy cold air moving into the **vacuum**, or empty space, left by the rising hot air. You can feel this movement when you are outside. If your back is to the wind, the air is rushing to fill in the low pressure area directly in front of you.

Everything around us is made up of small parts that we can't see without a powerful microscope. These small parts are called **molecules**. Let's pretend we are cold air molecules. When air molecules are cold, they get very close together and move very slowly. Let's put our hands down by our sides, get as close together as we can without touching one another, and move slowly around within a small area. Do you see how much space we take up? Not very much, do we? And how much do we weigh? It would be the sum of all our weights added together. Now let's pretend that the sun is warming us up and we will move a little further apart and move a little faster. We are warmer air now and take up more space, but we still weigh the same as we did when we were cold air. Now it is getting hotter and hotter, and we will move a little more quickly and a little further apart. We take up a lot more space now but we still weigh the same as we did when we were in a tiny area. For the space that it takes up, cold air weighs more than warm air because the molecules are so close together. When the molecules warm up and start moving faster, they get further apart, so the same size space becomes lighter. This process of heating and cooling of the air is what affects the direction and speed of the wind. As air cools, what happens to the air molecules? [*the molecules get closer together so the air is heavier and sinks down*] On the other hand, as air warms up, what happens to the air molecules? [*the molecules get further apart and the air is lighter and rises*] How does this cause wind? [*The cold air rushes in to fill the vacuum left by the rising hot air. This movement is what causes wind.*]

DIGGING DEEPER: 1. Watch the video, *Whirling Winds*, from Moody Institute of Science, 820 N. La Salle Blvd, Chicago, IL, 60610, 1995. 2. Read the section on "Weather & Climate" in the *Usborne Encyclopedia of Planet Earth*, EDC PUBLISHING, 10302 E. 55th Place, Tulsa, OK, 74146. (Usborne books do have evolutionary references, but these can provide opportunity for discussion of creation.) 3. Fly a kite and watch how the air currents affect the patterns of its flight.

Lesson 7:C Water and Weather

PREPARATION: *Copy this weather recipe onto the blackboard:* weather = sun + air + water + rotation & revolution + land. *You will need a small pan, a stove or electric burner for boiling water, a cookie sheet, ice cubes, a pot-holder, a glass of water, and an ice cube.*

INTRODUCTION and ACTIVITY: We would not have much difference in weather without water. Water is essential to all life and can be found in three different states. What is it called when it is a solid? [*ice*] What is it called when it is a liquid? [*water*] What is it called when it is a gas? [*steam or vapor*] Do you remember what we learned when we pretended to be air molecules? A similar thing happens with water molecules. When water molecules are cold, they get heavier and move more slowly. As the water molecules warm up, they move faster and further apart. Like the wind, the movement of cold to hot areas also occurs in the oceans. This movement causes the various ocean currents that affect the weather by cooling or warming the land near to them. The sun heats up the water and it evaporates (becomes a vapor). The tiny droplets of water vapor join to form clouds. When the droplets in the clouds get too heavy with moisture, they fall as precipitation, which means rain, sleet, or snow. Then the sun evaporates the water and the cycle begins again.

Let's do an experiment to show how this works. Look at an ice cube. The molecules are hardly moving. That is what keeps the water in the shape of an ice cube. Now let's heat up some ice in a small pan. See how the ice melts? As the ice warms up, the molecules of water can move faster. It is now a liquid and can move and change shape. As we continue to heat it, the molecules move faster and faster until they bump each other out of the pan. This is not smoke but water vapor. *(Caution: the steam and boiling water will burn the child if he gets too close.)* Carefully put your hand way above the pan and feel how wet your hand gets. *(Put several ice cubes onto a cookie sheet.)* Now we will hold the cookie sheet with some ice cubes on it over the steam. The steam (or water vapor) hits the cold cookie sheet, cools down, and turns back into a liquid and will drip down. We just made rain!

One of the fabulous facts of creation is that water is an amazing substance that actually becomes lighter in its solid state (which is ice) than when it is a liquid. As water gets colder, the molecules get closer so it is heavier and it sinks just like most substances. But just before water freezes into ice, the water molecules expand in volume and float to the top. (This means that, for the space they occupy, the frozen water molecules weigh less than warmer water because they are spread apart.) If the ice were heavier than water, the oceans, lakes and rivers would freeze from the bottom up and all the creatures that live in them would be frozen as well. Instead, the ice floats to the top and acts like a blanket, keeping the rest of the water below it warmer. If you want to see how this works, put an ice cube into a glass of water and watch it float. Why do you think that God planned it this way? [*So that water animals and plants are able to continue to live in the water below the surface, even in winter. In addition, the sun is able to melt the ice on top of the water easier than if it was deep down.*] With something as simple as water and ice we can see how God planned the smallest details of His creation!

SONG/POEM:

> **The Water Cycle**
> Let's take one little drop of rain
> And follow it to the ground again.
> It flows to the river and out to the sea,
> And evaporates, a cloud to be.
> Rain, rain that comes today,
> Will come back another way.

DIGGING DEEPER: 1. Research the difference between frozen fresh water and frozen ocean water. 2. Watch the video, *Where Waters Run* from Moody Institute of Science, 820 N. La Salle Blvd, Chicago, IL, 60610.

Lesson 7:D Rotation, Revolution, and Weather

PREPARATION: *Copy this weather recipe onto the blackboard:* weather = sun + air + water + rotation & revolution + land. *You will need a raw egg. You may want to do Lesson 7:D and 7:E at the same time.*

INTRODUCTION and ACTIVITY: Now we will try spinning a raw egg. It does not spin well, so force the egg to spin on its side with your hand. Then stop it by lightly placing your finger on top of it. Lift your finger up. What happens? [*the egg will start spinning again*] Why do you think the egg starts to spin again? [*It is because the liquid inside the egg is still spinning.*] On earth, the air and oceans are spinning at a different rate than the land. This is a main cause of the ocean and wind currents. This observation is called the Coriolis effect and accounts for the reason why cyclones are counterclockwise-rotating storms in the Northern Hemisphere, but rotate clockwise in the Southern Hemisphere.

Lesson 7:E Land and Weather

PREPARATION: *Student will need* **notebook pp. 39, 41-42**, *scissors, glue, crayons, pencil or pen. Copy this weather recipe onto the blackboard:* weather = sun + air + water + rotation & revolution + land.

INTRODUCTION: The last big ingredient affecting the weather is land. Mountains have an especially strong effect on the weather. Warm clouds gather water vapor from the oceans, but they must rise to go over the mountains. As the clouds go higher, they cool off. The molecules of water vapor get squeezed closer together and become drops of water again. These drops of water fall out of the clouds as rain before they pass over the mountains. Therefore the other side of a mountain is much drier. It is interesting to drive over a mountain range and see lush vegetation on one side and desert on the other. Land absorbs heat faster than water during the day, so it tends to be hotter over large land areas than over water. Land also loses heat faster than water at night, so it tends to get colder over large land areas faster at night.

We'll have a chance to review all the ingredients of weather a little later, but the next time you think about weather, try to remember all the different things that affect it.

BIBLE READING: *(Have student look up Scriptures.)* The Bible is an accurate source of information about the world around us. Hundreds of years ago, Job and Solomon described the water cycle. God's marvelous heater, the sun, causes the water to become a vapor. The process of evaporation cleans the salts and other impurities out of the water. The winds follow basic circuits and serve the purpose of bringing life-giving water back to the earth as rain (Jeremiah 10:13; Ecclesiastes 1:6). The rain and snow run off into rivers that run into the sea, and the process starts all over again (Ecclesiastes 1:7; Job 26:8, 36:27–29). What is the purpose of water? Water is essential for life. It cleanses our bodies (both inside and out) and makes plants grow (Isaiah 55:9–12). Jesus offered "living water" (John 4:7–14; Isaiah 55:1–2; Jeremiah 2:13) and His Word cleanses us spiritually like water does physically (Ephesians 5:26).

NOTEBOOK: *Weather Recipe, pp. 39, 41-42. The Weather Recipe* pages review all the things we discussed about weather. For the *Weather Recipe (page 2)*, cut along each of the dotted lines, and fold on the solid lines. Then glue each little booklet where it goes on the *Weather Recipe* page. On the empty front of each, draw and color in the symbol (picture) from the "weather recipe" that tells what is inside the booklet. Now, inside the booklets, fill in the blanks to complete each ingredient of the recipe. (***Answers:*** *Sun—sun, air, land, water, equator. Air—light, heavy. Water—rain, snow, clouds. Rotation—day, night, seasons. Land—mountains, rain, drier.*)

REVIEW: 1. What is weather? [*the condition of the atmosphere at a given time or place*]
2. What is the recipe for weather? [weather = sun + air + water + rotation & revolution + land]
3. How does the sun affect the weather? [*the sun provides heat and the angle of the sun's rays on the earth affect the amount of heat that is felt there*]
4. How does air affect the weather? [*the mixing of hot and cold air cause wind*]
5. How does water affect the weather? [*ocean currents cool or warm the land; evaporated water condenses and falls as precipitation*]
6. How does land affect the weather? [*land masses absorb heat or cold; generally, mountains keep precipitation on the side next to the ocean*]

Have the student explain his notebook page to a friend or relative and tell what he learned from the lesson. Also, review the songs/poems and activities.

DIGGING DEEPER: 1. Draw a map of the ocean currents and describe their effect on weather. 2. Do a report on the major wind currents and describe their effect on weather. 3. Find out about the weather phenomena of "El Niño" (refers to the Christ Child) and "La Niña", and give an oral report about them. 4. Do a study of the weather in your area for a particular month and compare it to the kind of weather typical for that month during the past ten years. See if you can discover any major differences and reasons for them. 5. How does weather affect various occupations? 6. What does the Bible have to say about weather?

LESSON 8: Clouds

PREPARATION: *Student will need notebook pp. 40, 43-47, and a pencil. Vocabulary words may be written on flash cards.*

VOCABULARY:

alto-: "higher" [L. *altus*, high]

cirrus or cirro-: "wispy" (delicate, fleecy, feathery clouds made up of ice crystals, "mares' tails," high altitude) [L. *cirrus*, a curl of hair]

cumulus or cumulo-: "puffed up" (dense puffs, mounds or towers of clouds with flat bases) [L. *cumulus*, a heap]

nimbus or nimbo-: "dark rain" (dense rain or snow cloud) [L. *numbus*, a cloud]

stratus or strato-: "layer" (straight layers of low altitude fog-like clouds) [L. *sternere*, to spread out]

Cloud names are combined to describe other types of clouds; nimbostratus, altocumulus, and so forth.

INTRODUCTION: In 1802, an Englishman named Luke Howard named the four main types of clouds. We still use these names and descriptions today. Most of the different types of clouds are named with combinations of these names. Many times we can observe several types of clouds in the sky at the same time. We will be going over each type and what its name means. Observing clouds is one of the ways we can predict the weather. Do you remember what causes clouds? [*Clouds are water vapor in the air.*] Warm air can hold a lot of droplets, and cold air cannot. Air currents cause the droplets to bump together and form larger droplets until they become big and heavy enough to fall. Clouds drop their water as rain, snow, hail or sleet.

SONG/POEM:

Not Just a Weatherman

"Cirrus" is the cloud that floats the highest in the sky,
It looks like wispy curls of smoke that scurry by.
Big fluffy cotton candy clouds are known as "cumulus,"
And "stratus" clouds are layered straight down close to us.

As weathermen who read the weather we can read God's signs,
He gives them in His Holy Book, His Spirit guides our minds.

Then "nimbus" means a cloud is dark and filled with rain or snow
And "alto" tells us clouds are high and not down low.
We put these words together and we can then define
All types of clouds and we can tell what weather we might find.

Don't just be a weatherman, but learn to read God's signs,
He gives them in His Holy Book, His Spirit guides our minds.

NOTEBOOK: *Cloud Cover, p. 40.* Write in the correct name of the basic cloud terms beside their definitions. The picture to the left will help you remember the different types.

[*Answers:* *cirrus, stratus, cumulus, nimbus*] Then use the parts of the definitions that are in quotations to write a definition of each cloud at the bottom left hand side. [*Answers:* *cirrocumulus clouds = wispy puffed-up clouds, altocumulus clouds = high puffed-up clouds, stratocumulus clouds = layer of puffed-up clouds, nimbostratus clouds = a dark rain layer of clouds, cumulonimbus clouds = puffed-up dark rain clouds*] Finally draw in the clouds using the definitions and the picture to help you. [*Pictures may vary.*]

BIBLE READING: *(Have student look up Scriptures.)* God is not in the wind, or the storm (1 Kings 19:9–12), but He is the Creator and Controller of the weather (Luke 8:22–25). There is no "Mother Nature." Job 37–39 tells us a lot about God causing the rain, snow, ice, and thunderstorms. However, even if we know all about the weather, what causes it, and how to predict it, that is not the most important thing for us to know. Jesus said that we need to be able to identify the spiritual warning signs and to observe the condition of our spiritual life (Matthew 16:2–3; Luke 12:56).

ACTIVITY: *Two Week Weather Chart, p. 47.* Weather is an important part of our everyday life. The weather helps us decide what clothes to wear, whether to play or work inside or outside, and it also can affect how we feel. For the next two weeks, you will be keeping track of the weather each day. Let's first write in the month. Then for each day, you will fill in the date and temperature. You can find out the temperature by looking at an outdoor thermometer, listening to the weather on radio or television, looking at the weather section of the newspaper, or calling the time and temperature telephone number in your area. Next you will draw the symbol for the kind of weather that day. Some days may have wind and sun, so you may draw more than one picture for each day. You may want to do another weather chart in a different season and look at the differences between them.

Cloud Detective, pp. 43-46. On the days that there are interesting clouds, fill out a *Cloud Detective* page to go with your weather chart. Look at the basic shape of the cloud and mark the closest one. How high is the cloud? There are three basic heights or altitudes; close to the ground, medium heights, and very high altitudes. Mark the approximate altitude. From the "Basic Cloud Shape" column, come down to the approximate "Altitude" and find the name of the cloud. Write the name in the top left-hand corner. What is the color of the cloud? How fast is it moving? And which direction? What is the approximate wind speed? [*Use Beaufort's chart on the Speed Detective p. 49 to estimate the wind speed.*] Fill in the answers and keep these pages with your *Two Week Weather Chart.*

REVIEW: 1. What is a cloud? [*clouds are water vapor in the air*]
2. How is a cloud formed? [*The sun heats up water and it evaporates. The tiny droplets of water vapor join to form clouds.*]
3. Name five different types of clouds. [*cirrocumulus, altocumulus, stratocumulus, nimbostratus, cumulonimbus*]
4. Describe a cumulus cloud. [*dense puffs, mounds or towers of clouds with flat bases*]
5. What kind of a cloud is a stratus cloud? [*straight layers of low altitude fog-like clouds*]

Have the student explain his notebook page to a friend or relative and tell what he learned from the lesson. Also, review the songs/poems and activities.

DIGGING DEEPER: 1. Visit a weather station. 2. Listen to the weather channel on radio or television. 3. Research the different types of equipment used to predict weather, such as a barometer, a weather satellite, weather radar, thermometer, weather vane and so forth. Get a book (like a "Boy Scout" manual) on how to make your own weather equipment with things around the house. 4. Check out *The Weather Book* by Michael Oard, Master Books, Green Forest, AR, 1997.

LESSON 9: The Speed of Light, Sound and Wind

PREPARATION: *Student will need* **notebook p. 49** *and a pencil. Vocabulary words may be written on flash cards.*

VOCABULARY:
> **light:** energy that travels in waves, mostly from the sun, and travels very fast (186,200 miles per second) [O.E. *leoht*, light]
> **omnipresent:** present in all places at the same time [L. *omnis*, all + *praesens*, being present]

INTRODUCTION: Do you know what the word "**omnipresent**" means? The first part, "omni" means "all," so the word means "present everywhere." That is one of the characteristics of God. We can't be everywhere at once, we can't see everything at once, and we can't hear everything at once. Speed is a measurement of the time that it takes to go from one point to another. For us, time must pass before we get from one place to another. When we travel in a car, we often travel 70 miles in one hour. In an airplane, we can travel at greater speeds, and in a rocket, even greater.

Light, sound, and wind must travel to get from one place to another also. You will be learning about the speed at which each of these travels. Which do you think travels the fastest? [*light*] Which travels the slowest? [*wind*] The **speed of wind** varies with the weather. On a calm day you are able to walk or run faster than the wind. You would need a car or an airplane to outrun the gale winds of a large storm. In 1947, a pilot by the name of Chuck Yeager became the first man to fly faster than the speed of sound. His plane was shaking as he reached the **speed of sound**. Other planes had been broken to bits by the force of the sound wave. When he went faster than sound, the air became calmer. No person, however, has been able to travel at the **speed of light**.

SONG/POEM:
> ### God is Light
> God says in His Word He is light,
> And it's true that He gives us our sight.
> For our physical eyes, He shows us our way,
> And our spirit He leads every day.
>
> God says there's no darkness in Him,
> He has no hidden shadows within.
> He's transparently Holy, He's wondrously pure,
> And His promise to guard us is sure.

God sees the same if it's night or it's day,
If we're home or we're far away,
He made us and knows us, and He loves us so,
He wants us His love to know.

BIBLE READING: *(Have student look up Scriptures.)*   The Risen Savior, Jesus Christ was able to go instantly from one place to another (Luke 24, 31, 36, 51; John 20:26; Acts 1:9). Philip was also miraculously transported from one place to another after he had talked to the Ethiopian man in the desert (Acts 8:39–40). However, until we receive our new bodies, we will probably have to travel by ordinary means to get from one place to another. But no matter where we go, God is always there with us (Psalm 121:5–8; 139:7–12). God's Word is a light for our path, and He shows us where He wants us to go (Proverbs 20:24, Psalm 23:3; 119:105).

NOTEBOOK: *Speed Detective, p. 49.*   **Speed of Light:** Light travels approximately 186,000 miles per second. If we were traveling at the speed of light, we could circle around the earth 7 1/3 times in just one second. We measure how far away stars are in "light-years" (the distance light travels in a year). It takes 8 1/3 minutes for light to reach us from the sun. To reach the next closest star, Alpha Centauri, would take us more than 5 years traveling at the speed of light. On your *Speed Detective* notebook page, find the "Speed of Light" box. I will count each second out loud as you trace the loops around the earth. When you finish, write down the number of seconds it took. Then we'll figure out from the chart below it, about how many times around the earth you could have traveled at the speed of light, in the amount of time it took to go through the maze. [*Count each second aloud till all have finished the maze.*] For example, if it took 25 seconds to trace the maze, find 25 seconds on the chart and color in the whole row across. In the 25 seconds it took you to trace the maze, light traveled 4,657,000 miles and if you had been traveling at the speed of light, you would have gone around the world 183 1/3 times.

Speed of Sound: Sound travels fast, but not nearly as fast as light. That is why you always see the lightning before you hear the thunder. In one second, sound travels 1/5 of a mile, or one mile every five seconds. The next time you are in a thunderstorm, remember this easy way to figure out how far away the lightning is: From the moment you see the lightning until you hear the thunder, count each second by saying "Thunderstorm one, thunderstorm two", and so forth. Then divide the total number of seconds by five to get the number of miles. We can practice now by filling in the chart on the "Speed of Sound" box on your page. Figure out the correct numbers to fill in on the blank spaces.

Miles	1	2	3	4	5	6	7	8
Seconds	5	10	15	20	25	30	35	40

Speed of Wind: Although we can't actually see the wind, we can see its effects. Air can be so calm and still that nothing moves, or it can move so fast that it knocks down trees and buildings. Hurricanes and tornadoes are winds that blow in tight circles at very high speeds.

Wind is caused when the sun's rays heat the air in certain areas. The warm air rises and expands and as cold air moves into the warm air space, the result is wind. You can measure the approximate speed of the wind by using a chart developed by a man named Beaufort. By watching the effect of the wind on trees and other things around, you can come very close to figuring out the speed of the wind. Let's read through the chart on the "Speed of Wind" in your notebook and then you can figure out the wind speed for each picture. [*Answers:* *8–12 m.p.h., 32–38 m.p.h., 0 m.p.h., 39–46 m.p.h., 55–up m.p.h., 25–31 m.p.h., 1–3 m.p.h., 47–54 m.p.h.*] Let's look outside right now and see if we can estimate the wind speed.

REVIEW: 1. How are distances in space measured? [*"light-years"—the distance light travels in a year*]

2. True or false: No one has ever been able to travel at the speed of sound. [*false*]

3. How can you estimate how far away lightning is from you? [*count each second from the moment you see the lightning until you hear the thunder, then divide by five*]

4. What causes wind? [*as warm air rises and expands, cold air rushes in to fill the vacuum, resulting in wind*]

5. How can you estimate the speed of the wind? [*Beaufort's Chart; watching the effect of the wind on trees and other objects*]

TEST: *Student will need **notebook p. 248,** Crossword Review 4. Use as a review or test for older students. **Answers:** Teacher's p. 124.*

Have the student explain his notebook page to a friend or relative.

DIGGING DEEPER: 1. Do a research project on hurricanes (where they occur, when they occur, and how they are identified, etc.). 2. Write a paper about how wind has been harnessed for energy and think of a new application for wind (windmills, wind instruments, and so forth). 3. Make a small windmill out of things you can find around the house. 4. Find out how sound travels and how humans and animals are able to hear sounds. 5. Fill out a *Scientist Detective* page for one of these: Luke Howard (1772-1864), the cloud man; Christiaan Huygens (1629-1695), developer of the wave theory of light; James Clerk Maxwell (1831-1879), who developed equations for magnetism, electricity and light; Albert Einstein (1897–1955), the scientist who discovered how light travels (the theory of relativity). 6. Research the Fujita Tornado Damage Scale. Find out about the Japanese man, Tetsuya Theodore Fujita, who developed the scale, and what the classifications mean.

THE PLANT KINGDOM

LESSON 10: Plants

Plants will be covered in three lessons.

Lesson 10:A Photosynthetic Plants

PREPARATION: *You will need a small section of grass with its roots, a stalk of celery, and a glass of water with red food coloring. Optional: Things for a small terrarium such as a large glass jar with a lid, small rocks, potting soil or backyard dirt, and several small plants. Vocabulary words may be written on flash cards.*

VOCABULARY:

> **chlorophyll**: the green color in plants which traps sunlight and makes photosynthesis possible [Gk. *chloros*, green + *phyllon*, leaf]
> **cohesion**: sticking together [L. *cohaerere*, to stick together]
> **photosynthesis**: the process by which a plant creates carbohydrates [Gk. *photo*, light + *syn*, together + *thesis*, a placing]

INTRODUCTION: Without plants, life would be impossible on our planet. Plants provide not only food, clothing, medicines, and shelter, but also the very oxygen that we breathe. Only plants are able to produce their own food and subsequently provide food for all the animals and peoples of the world as well.

Each part of the plant serves a special purpose. Millions of rootlets push their way through the hard soil and can even crack through rocks. These tiny root hairs take in water and minerals from under the soil. The water molecules are held together by **cohesion** and are pulled up through the stem (in a flower) or trunk (in a tree) as water evaporates from the leaves. The process is very much like sucking water up through a straw. Because the suction is so great, water can be pulled over two hundred feet to the top of the tallest trees in one hour. Water vapor from the leaves is put back into the air, continuing the water cycle.

Leaves are food factories. Leaves absorb carbon dioxide from the air, and their green coloring, called **chlorophyll**, traps energy from the sunlight. The sun's energy and the carbon dioxide are transformed into energy-rich sugars, or food (carbohydrates). This process is called **photosynthesis** and involves at least seventy separate chemical reactions. Photosynthesis is so complicated that scientists have not been able to duplicate it in a laboratory with all their equipment, but it is all done automatically in a simple, tiny cell of a plant. One of the "waste products" of this process is oxygen, the gas we must breathe in order to live. The atmosphere would have no free oxygen without plants. Because of their activity, one out of every five molecules of the air surrounding us is oxygen.

ACTIVITY: Let's look at the root hairs of some grass and see the part of the plant that picks up water and minerals. Isn't it incredible that those tiny hairs can do such a good job? Now, put a stalk of celery into the glass of water with food coloring in it. Let it stay there for an hour and then check back to see what has happened. (*After an hour, check the celery.*) Do you see how it has sucked up the colored water? This is an example of cohesion and it has shown us how water is able to travel upward through the plants and trees. (*Optional: Set up a little terrarium and see how plants recycle water and air. Take a glass jar and carefully make a layer of small rocks. Now add soil. With a small stick or knife, plant little plants. Water the plants well and then put the lid on. Watch what happens during the next few weeks.*)

BIBLE READING: (*Have student look up Scriptures.*) There are so many pictures of our spiritual lives that can be better understood by observing plants. We are told to be "rooted and established in love" (Ephesians 3:17–19; Colossians 2:6–7). Jesus refers to himself as "the true vine" and we are like the branches (John 15:1–11). In fact, He says that every plant that the Heavenly Father didn't plant will be rooted up (Matthew 15:13). And every tree that doesn't produce good fruit will be cut down (Matthew 3:10, 7:19; Luke 3:9). Let's be like heavenly plants and produce the fruit of the Spirit and life-giving air by the words we speak!

REVIEW: 1. What do plants provide and do for us? [*they provide food, clothing, medicines, shelter, and manufacture oxygen*]
2. What is photosynthesis? [*the process by which a plant creates carbohydrates*]
    What is one of the waste products? [*oxygen*]
3. How does water get from the roots to the leaves of a plant? [*by the process of cohesion*]

DIGGING DEEPER: 1. Enjoy coloring and studying the *Botany Coloring Book* by Paul Young, Harper Perennial, HarperCollins Publishers, Inc, 10 East 53rd St, New York, NY, 10022, 1982. 2. Watch the video, *Planet Earth*, from Moody Institute of Science, 820 N. La Salle Blvd, Chicago, IL, 60610, 1995. 3. Check out Chapter 7 in *Lyrical Life Science*, by Doug and Dorry Eldon, Lyrical Learning, 8008 Cardwell Hill, Corvallis, OR 97330, 1996.

Lesson 10:B Flowers

PREPARATION: *Student will need **notebook pp. 50-63**, scissors, crayons, glue, salt (or pollen from a flower), and perfume (optional). Also, he will need some actual flowers or pictures of flowers to work with. Clear sticky-backed plastic will allow him to display collected flowers. You might also want to have some flower seeds to plant in a pot or in the garden. A field book on flowers would be helpful. Vocabulary words may be written on flash cards.*

VOCABULARY:
    fertilize: to make fruitful or able to reproduce [L. *fertilis*, fruitful]
    flower: the part of the plant that produces seeds [L. *flox*, flower]
    petal: the colored flower-leaf [Gk. *petalon*, a thin plate]
    pistil: the seed-bearing organ of a flower [L. *pistillum*, a pestle]
    pollen: the fertilizing dust in a flower [L. *pollen*, fine flour]
    root: the part of the plant that seeks nourishment for the plant; generally grows
        underground [O.E. *wyrt*, root]

stamen: the pollen-bearing part of a flower [L. *stamen*, fiber, thread]
stem: the stalk of a plant [O.E. *stefn*, stem]

INTRODUCTION: The **flower** is the part of a flowering plant that makes seeds so that new plants can grow. Many flowers have **petals** that are just the right color, shape and smell to attract insects to pollinate them. The **stamen** makes a dust-like substance called **pollen**. Pollen is carried from flower to flower by wind or insects. Inside the flower, the pollen travels down a long tube called the **pistil** to **fertilize** the egg cells. The fertilized egg cells develop into seeds. These tiny seeds can then grow into whole new plants. Many times the seeds are inside what we call fruit (like plums and peaches). Sometimes we eat the seeds themselves (like grains of wheat, corn, and nuts).

SONG/POEM:

Bear Fruit

Behold the sower went out to sow,
And some seeds fell by the road.
The birds came by and ate them up,
And none were left, we're told.
And other seeds fell on the rocks
And quickly grew, then died
Because their roots could not survive the sun.

So don't let lack of understanding or shallowness of root,
Or cares or riches of this world keep you from bearing fruit,
But let the love of Jesus grow down deep so you can stay alive
And you can bear a hundred fold of fruit for Him.

Still other seeds fell in the thorns,
And the thorns soon choked them out.
But other seeds fell in good soil,
That's what this song's about.
The good soil yielded forth a crop
Some even a hundred fold,
Some sixty and some thirty times the start.

So don't let lack of understanding or shallowness of root,
Or cares or riches of this world keep you from bearing fruit,
But let the love of Jesus grow down deep so you can stay alive
And you can bear a hundred fold of fruit for Him.

ACTIVITY: Plants make their own food and provide food for all living creatures. Animals either eat plants or they eat other animals that eat plants. Make a list of the different kinds of food that come from plants and list them by the parts. Here is a chart to help get you started. *(Write only the headings of the following chart on the blackboard or a large piece of paper. Randomly read the names of different foods and have the student write them in under the correct heading either on the blackboard or at their desks.)*

Seed	Leaves	Stems	Flower	Fruit	Roots
corn	lettuce	sugar cane	broccoli	berries	carrots
wheat	spinach	rhubarb	cauliflower	apples	beets
rice	chard	celery	squash	apricots	turnips
oats	cabbage	asparagus	blossom	plums	radishes
peas	tea leaves	*potatoes	artichokes	peaches	sweet
nuts	mint	bamboo		dates	potatoes
peanuts		shoots		figs	
coffee		onions		pears	
cocoa				bananas	
pepper		*Yes, potatoes		oranges	
		are stems not		tomatoes	
		roots.		green beans	
				okra	

NOTEBOOK: *Plant Parts, p. 50-52.* Color and then cut out the flower parts and the bee from *Plant Parts (page 2)* in your notebook. Fold them as directed along the dotted lines and then glue them on the *Plant Parts* page. *(Have students read over the completed page separately or as a class.)*

(Use the following paragraph to aid in the concluding discussion.) Could life exist without plants? [*No*] Why are plants so important? [*There would be no food or oxygen without them. They also help create the ozone layer which protects us from radiation.*] What ingredients do plants use to produce food by photosynthesis? [*Plants produce food with sunlight and carbon dioxide. They give off oxygen and water vapor as by-products.*] Where does photosynthesis take place? [*With the chlorophyll in the cells or tiny inner parts of the leaves.*] What is the purpose of the flower? [*It is to produce seeds so that more plants of its kind can grow.*] In order to do this, the flower must be pollinated. What is pollen? [*Pollen is a dust-like substance that is carried from flower to flower by wind and insects. It fertilizes the egg cells, and then seeds form in the pistil of the flower.*] What do the roots do? [*The roots take in water and minerals for the plant.*]

Flower Detective and *Portrait of a Flower pp. 54-63.* God has a lot of variety in His creation. But He also has patterns that He repeats. To understand nature and God's plan of design, we need to look closely and compare what things are the same and what are different. To be a flower detective you need to look carefully at plants and record what you see. The *Flower Detective* pages will help you do this. Choose a flowering plant (*either a picture from a book or a live plant*). Draw and color this plant on the *Portrait of a Flower* page preceding it. Don't worry about the name of the plant or the plant family quite yet.

   ☑Look at the leaf arrangement on the plant you selected. Are the leaves alternately placed on the stem? Are they opposite? Are they whorled?

   ☑Look at the shape of the leaves. Find the one that matches the closest.

   ☑Now look at the leaf again. Is it simple, toothed, or does it have lobes? Are there three, five, or more leaves on one stem? Color the shape on the *Flower Detective* page that best matches the details on the leaf and stem.

   ☑Now examine the flower. What color is it? How is it placed on the stem? Is there one flower at the top, or several in different places? Some flowers look like a single flower but are really a head that is made up of many tiny flowers. There may be extra-large petals around the head. (An example is a sunflower or dandelion.)

☑What is the shape of your flower's petals? Now use a field guide for flowers to find the name of the plant and the plant family for your flower.

Find and draw (or mount*) another flower on the next *Portrait of a Flower* page and analyze it on the subsequent *Flower Detective* page. [*You can mount them by covering them with clear sticky-backed plastic.*] Wild flowers are especially interesting to study and different regions of the country often have their own field guides describing the varieties unique to the area.

(*Find out if there are any restrictions for picking wild flowers in your area. Also, caution the student not to pick flowers from others' yards without permission.)

BIBLE READING: *(Have student look up Scriptures.)* Jesus is called "the Rose of Sharon" and "the Lily of the valley." He stated that even Solomon, the king, in all his glory could not compare to the lilies of the field (Matthew 6:25–34). How marvelously God provides for our needs, just as He provides for all of His creation (Psalm 104). The story of the sower who sowed his seed is rich with food for thought (Matthew 13:3–9, 18–24; Mark 4:1–20). God is the One who provides the seeds, not only for actual plants, but also seeds of righteousness (2 Corinthians 9:10; 1 Peter 1:23–25). Jesus said that we will be known by our fruit (Matthew 7:16–20) and the kind of fruit we should be producing is the fruit of the Holy Spirit in our lives (love, joy, peace, patience, kindness, goodness, faithfulness, gentleness and self-control, Galatians 5:22).

REVIEW: 1. What is a flower? [*the part of the plant that produces seeds*]
2. What are two ways that a flower can be fertilized? [*by wind and insects*]
3. What are three features that you could use to describe a particular flower? [*leaf placement, leaf shape and edge, flower placement, petal shape*]
4. Name the parts of a flower. [*petal, pistil, stamen, pollen, egg cells*]

Have the student explain his notebook page to a friend or relative and tell what he learned from the lesson. Also, review the songs/poems and activities.

DIGGING DEEPER: 1. Learn to identify the common wildflowers in your area. 2. Play a game called *The Pollination Game* from Ampersand Press, 750 Lake St., Port Townsend, WA, 98368. 3. A flower can be carefully pressed between sheets of newspaper laid under a stack of heavy, large books. Change the newspaper after a few days to extract moisture. The dried, flattened flower can be laid on a sheet of paper and covered with clear sticky-backed plastic for display. 4. Dissect several different types of flowers and identify the internal structures. 5. Write a report on how herbs, plants and flowers are used for medicinal purposes. 6. Plant some flowers or vegetables in your garden or flowerpot. *(Having a garden is a wonderful opportunity to explain many spiritual principles to children. Not only do they have an opportunity to be responsible in caring for a garden, but it also provides ready made and understandable applications of biblical truths.)* 7. Read Chapters 5 and 6 of *The Forever Feast*, by Dr. Paul Brand, Vine Books, Servant Publications, Ann Arbor, MI 1993. 8. Fill out a *Scientist Detective* page on one of these: George Washington Carver (1864-1943), who discovered hundreds of uses for peanuts; Luther Burbank (1849-1926), who worked with plant genetics; John Ray (1627-1705), who first classified plants; Nehemiah Grew (1641-1712), co-founder of plant anatomy.

Lesson 10:C Fungus Plants

PREPARATION: *You will need ingredients and utensils for a yeast bread recipe, some water, scraps of cotton cloth, some moldy and fresh bread, and some small plastic containers or plastic bags. Student will need* **notebook p. 65.** *Vocabulary words may be written on flash cards.*

VOCABULARY:

algae: very simple photosynthetic plants found in water or damp places, containing chlorophyll and other pigments (colorings), and having no true roots, stems, leaves or seeds (L. *alga*, seaweed]

fungus: a very simple plant that does not produce food by photosynthesis, but feeds on living or dead plants or animals; it does not have true roots, stems, leaves, seeds or chlorophyll, and reproduces by means of spores; **fungi** is the plural word [L. *fungus*, mushroom or fungus]

spores: cells sent out by bacteria, fungi, algae, mosses, ferns and so forth, capable of developing into new adult plants [Gk. *spora*, a sowing]

INTRODUCTION: Most plants make their own food with green chlorophyll, water, air and energy from the sun, but some do not. **Algae** are very tiny simple plants with no true roots, stems, leaves or seeds. Like most plants, they use chlorophyll and other colorings to make their own food (photosynthesis). **Fungi** are very small plants with a similar structure which do not contain chlorophyll. They feed on other plants or animals. Many fungi are harmful, causing disease or allergies, spoiling foods, or damaging plant and animal products such as paper, cloth, wood and leather. Other fungi are helpful and include yeast, edible mushrooms, and the fungi used for making cheese and penicillin. Both fungi and algae reproduce by sending out one-celled **spores**, which are capable of developing into new adult plants, some right away, and some after a period of time (dormancy).

ACTIVITY: Let's grow some fungi. First we'll make a yeast mixture. *(Use a bread dough recipe or mix 1/2 cup lukewarm water with two teaspoons sugar and one tablespoon active yeast. Set the yeast mixture aside for a few minutes.)* Now, dip a scrap of cotton cloth in some water, wad it up, and hide it in a plastic bag in a warm, dark place. After a few days, we'll check to see what happened to the cloth. You will then understand why you need to be careful not to leave your wet clothes where they can't get dry. *(Keep the cloth away from other clothes so the fungi won't spread.)* Finally, let's place some moldy food, like bread or cheese, inside a container or plastic bag. We'll add a fresh piece of bread *(homemade bread, without the preservatives of "store-bought" bread, works the fastest)* and close the container tightly. Put it in a warm, dark place, away from other foods. *(It will even work in the refrigerator, unfortunately!)* We'll check that bread in a few days too. Now, let's see what the yeast has done. *(You may wish to continue with your bread recipe and enjoy a snack!)* Don't forget to check the cloth and the bread in a day or two. You can keep track of what you find growing on the bread with your *Mold Detective* page. Be sure to check the items every day and record what you see. When the mold spreads to the fresh food, and the cloth develops a good colony of mildew, throw them away. Be sure not to let the spores travel to other plant or animal products nearby, for each spore is capable of starting a new plant.

SONG/POEM:

Clean

My bread is old, it's growing mold,
I'll have to throw it away.
I found mildew in the tennis shoe
I wanted to wear today.

My mother told me she was cold,
A fire would feel real good.
It wouldn't start, the logs fell apart.
A fungus had rotted the wood.

Along came sin; Adam let it in.
It destroyed his walk with God.
God cursed the ground, and Adam found
Thorny weeds taking over the sod.

When Moses heard God's powerful Word,
He told the people plain,
"If you obey and walk God's way,
You'll be blessed with crops and rain."

But they also heard the warning word,
"If you will not obey,
You are under a curse, it will get much worse,
There will come mildew and decay."

Now I understand it is by God's hand
That the mold and fungus grow.
It's a lesson on sin: If I let it stay in,
It will ruin my life, I know.

My bread I threw, with the tennis shoe,
On the pile of rotten wood.
I confessed my sin, Jesus Christ came in.
I will walk with Him for good.

NOTEBOOK: *Mold Detective, p. 65.* Unlike the green (photosynthetic) plants you just studied, fungus does not produce its own food and does not need sunshine. Molds belong to the fungus family. On the *Mold Detective* page, you will be recording your observations of the mold that grows on the piece of bread you prepared *(for the lesson's ACTIVITY)*. Draw and color the growth of the mold on the "piece of bread" and in the circle, draw a close-up of what you see with a magnifying glass (or microscope, if available). (Laboratories do similar experiments to see what organisms are present in a given specimen. Instead of a slice of bread, they grow the "cultures" on a gelatin-like substance called an agar plate.)

BIBLE READING: *(Have student look up Scriptures.)* The Bible is clear about the harmful and the beneficial effects of fungi (Matthew 13:33; 1 Corinthians 5:6). Many of the passages present mold and mildew as a punishment from God for the disobedience of His people (Deuteronomy 28:22; Amos 4:9; Haggai 2:17). Others present it like sin, contamination that had to be cleansed (Leviticus 13:47–59, 14:33–57). Jesus taught His disciples to "guard against the yeast of the Pharisees and Sadducees." (Matthew 16:6–12). The celebration of the Passover required that all yeast be cleansed from the Jewish home (Exodus 12:15). Since Jesus Christ, the Passover Lamb, has been sacrificed, we are to live our lives without the "yeast of malice and wickedness," and as the bread without yeast (unleavened bread or "matzah"), the bread of sincerity and truth (1 Corinthians 5:7–8).

REVIEW: 1. How is fungus different from green plants? [*it does not produce food by photosynthesis, but feeds on other plants or animals*]
2. What are some good and helpful uses for fungus? [*yeast for bread, edible mushrooms, fungi for making cheese and penicillin*]
3. What are some harmful effects of fungus? [*causes disease and allergies, spoils food, damages plant and animal products*]
4. How do fungi, algae, mosses, and ferns reproduce? [*through spores*]
5. What is algae? [*simple photosynthetic plants found in water or damp places*]

Have the student explain his notebook page to a friend or relative and tell what he learned from the lesson. Also, review the songs/poems and activities.

DIGGING DEEPER: 1. Draw pictures of different types of mushrooms, poisonous and edible, and their uses. 2. Go for a walk in the woods, turning over fallen logs, searching for signs of fungal activity and mushrooms. (Do not pick any, as some may be poisonous.) 3. Write a report on diseases caused by fungus and yeast (such as athlete's foot, candida, and so forth). 4. Study how various types of cheese are made. Then sample several different kinds and record the name, flavor, color, and texture of each one. 5. Fill out a *Scientist Detective* page for Sir Alexander Fleming (1881–1955), the British discoverer of penicillin or Anton Van Leeuwenhoek (1632–1723), who discovered microorganisms with a microscope. 6. Check out Chapter 6 in *Lyrical Life Science*, by Doug and Dorry Eldon, Lyrical Learning, 8008 Cardwell Hill, Corvallis, OR 97330, 1996, www.lyricallearning.com..

*winter
& fall
2010
Also
9-9-09*

LESSON 11: Trees

PREPARATION: *Student will need* **notebook pp. 66-75**, *crayons, clear sticky-backed plastic, and a pencil. A field guide on trees would be helpful. Also, plan an outing to observe various types of trees, or get pictures of trees to work with as well as a slice of wood that shows the rings (such as firewood or the end of a board). Vocabulary words may be written on flash cards.*

VOCABULARY:

> **tree**: a plant with a woody trunk [O.E. *treow*, a tree]
>
> **deciduous trees**: trees that shed their leaves in autumn, generally broadleaf
> hardwoods [L. *decidere*, to fall down]
>
> **evergreen trees**: trees that keep their leaves the year round, generally needle-leaved
> conifers (cone-bearing trees)
>
> **tropical trees**: trees in areas that are warm all year, usually broadleaf evergreen trees

INTRODUCTION and ACTIVITY: A **tree** is a plant with a woody trunk. Most trees mature in 50 to 100 years. There are some sequoia trees that are over 2,000 years old and are more than 300 feet tall. The oldest known trees are bristle cone pines, some of which are about 5,000 years old! You can tell the age of some trees from the rings in their trunks. If you cut a slice of the trunk horizontally you can see these circles. Let's look at a slice of wood together. *(Point out the rings in the wood.)* In areas that have four seasons, trees are dormant, or sleeping, during the winter. Trees grow wood only in late spring and early summer. The wood changes from the beginning to the end of the growing season, causing the characteristic rings of each species. Together, a light and dark ring show one year's growth. When trees are crowded, they grow more slowly. The size of their growth rings show gradual changes in how much sunlight the trees were able to receive. In general, having enough space to grow is the most important factor in the growth rate of a tree.

There are three main types of trees. **Deciduous** trees are hardwood broadleaf trees that generally lose their leaves every autumn. Their wood is usually hard and is useful in making lumber for furniture, flooring and packing materials. Some deciduous trees produce fruit, such as apples and cherries. **Evergreen** trees, as their name implies, do not lose their leaves in the fall but stay green the year round. They have narrow leaves that lose less water so they do not dry out in the winter. Their wood is softer and provides lumber used for construction. Low quality trees and logs, and lumber by-products from both hardwood and softwoods, are used to make paper. **Tropical** trees are broadleaf evergreens and include lemon and avocado trees. They grow in tropical regions where seasonal changes are mild, and because they grow all year, there is no annual change in the wood to make a growth ring. Sometimes cactus and palm trees are considered types of trees, but they are not true trees.

NOTEBOOK: *Tree Detective, pp. 66-75.* Choose a tree you would like to study. Collect a leaf of it if possible. Get a *Tree Detective* page and we will work through it together. Lay your leaf on the back of the preceding notebook page and cover it with clear sticky-backed plastic. Do not try to name the tree until you have finished studying it.

> ☑ Which type of tree is it; deciduous, evergreen or tropical?
>
> ☑ What type of bark does it have; smooth, rough, or peeling? Color in the type of bark

that matches most closely, or draw in your own.

☑ What is the overall shape of the tree; pointed, spreading or round? Color in the closest match, or draw in your own.

☑ Now look at the shape of the leaves. What is the leaf arrangement, alternate, opposite each other or whorled? Circle one.

☑ Next match the leaf complexity. Is it simple, toothed, or lobed?

☑ How many leaves are on a stem?

☑ Color in the type of nuts, cones or fruit your tree produces. The three fruit types are a drupe (which has one seed in the middle, like a peach), a berry (which has seeds all through it), and a pome (which has a core with the seeds in it, like an apple).

Now, with all this information, see if you can find the name of your tree in a field guide for trees. Practice observing and identifying other types of trees.

BIBLE READING: *(Have student look up Scriptures.)* What are some types of trees and uses of wood mentioned in the Bible? (*The Tree of the Knowledge of Good and Evil and the ark are some examples.*) If we find our continual delight in God's Word, we will be like trees planted by streams of water, producing good fruit in our lives. Let's read Psalm 1 and Galatians 5:22 together.

EVOLUTION STUMPERS: The oldest known trees are the bristle cone pine trees of California, which are accurately dated by their rings at about 5,000 years old. They are hardy enough to last several more thousand years, if nothing harms them. Why aren't there any groves of trees that date further back? (*Hint: How long ago was the flood?*)

REVIEW: 1. What is a tree? [*a plant with a woody trunk*]
2. What are three types of trees? [*deciduous, evergreen, tropical*]
3. What is the difference between a deciduous and an evergreen tree? [*a deciduous tree sheds its leaves in autumn, an evergreen tree does not*]
4. Tell me four characteristics that you can examine in order to identify a tree. [*type of bark, shape of tree, shape and complexity of leaves, arrangement of leaves, nuts/cones/fruit*]
5. What are two things you can tell about a tree from its rings? [*how old it is and how much sunshine it was able to receive*]
6. What is the most important factor in the growth rate (size of the growth ring) of a tree? [*ample space to grow; lack of crowding*]

Have the student explain his notebook page to a friend or relative and tell what he learned from the lesson. Also, review the songs/poems and activities.

DIGGING DEEPER: 1. Plant a tree. 2. Make a list of the many things that trees can provide for humans as well as animals. 3. Learn how to graft a branch onto a tree and how to prune a tree correctly. 4. Memorize or write a poem about trees. 5. Get samples of several types of trees and learn to recognize their color, texture, hardness, and use. 6. Identify all the trees in your neighborhood. 7. Summarize, in an outline form, the preparation and requirements that are needed to become a forest ranger. 8. Take a trip to your local plant nursery and ask about the types of trees that do well in your area. 9. Find out about tree celebrations such as the American "Arbor Day" and the Jewish "Tu Bishvat" ("The New Year of Trees").

LESSON 12: PLANT ECOLOGY: Flora and Fauna

PREPARATION: *Student will need* **notebook p. 76** *and crayons. Vocabulary words may be written on flash cards.*

VOCABULARY:

desert: an area, either cold or hot, which lacks moisture most of the year
[L. *deserere*, to abandon]

monsoon region: a hot region with distinct wet and dry seasons

mountain region: the 25% of earth's land surface over 3,300 feet above sea level, with plant and animal life varying according to altitude

polar: refers to the North (Arctic) and South (Antarctic) Poles [Gk. *polos*, a pivot]

savanna: a warm area with wet and dry seasons, scrub type plants and only scattered trees

taiga: coniferous (cone-bearing) forest below the Arctic region [Russ. *taiga*, coniferous forest]

temperate forest: a deciduous forest in a region that has four seasons

temperate grassland: a plain of grasses where not enough rain falls to sustain a forest, but which has more rain than a desert.

tropical rain forest: a hot area with heavy (59–78 inches) rainfall, teeming with plant and animal life

tundra: treeless plains in the Arctic Circle [Russ. *tundra*, a marsh]

INTRODUCTION and ACTIVITY: Plants are found in every region of the earth, from the oceans to the mountains, from the snow fields of the poles to the sands of the deserts. Each plant is uniquely adapted to the climate and soil of the region it inhabits. For example, in the desert, some seeds lie dormant until exactly the right amount of rain has fallen. They wait until enough water is available to survive. Even on glaciers, tiny lichens flourish, providing nourishment for the animals of the area. With incredible variety and order, plants demonstrate the design of our Creator. Plant life is directly related to moisture and temperature. Deserts are found in the same longitudes (imaginary lines dividing the earth horizontally) as rain forests. Trees can put literally tons of water vapor into the air, thus creating their own wet climate. When trees are replanted in a desert area, it is possible to reclaim the desert. Plants interact with each other in many ways to preserve themselves. Taller plants shield smaller ones and together they promote the moisture and climate they each need. We call plant life, "flora", and animal life, "fauna." The types of plants determine the kinds and numbers of animals that can live in an area. For example, there are relatively few animals living in a desert compared to the number of animals that live in a tropical rain forest. When the ecological balance of an area is upset by natural or human causes, many new types of interdependencies develop as plant and animal life adapt to new conditions.

BIBLE READING: *(Have student look up Scriptures.)* God cares for all His creation and its special needs (Psalm 104). He placed the first man in charge of His creation. Adam named and cared for God's creatures. We have a responsibility to be good caretakers of God's creation. However, although we should understand and practice conservation, it remains God's good pleasure to bring us rain and crops (Deuteronomy 11:17, 28:12; Psalm 107:33–38; Matthew 5:44–45).

NOTEBOOK: *Plant Life on our Planet, p. 52.* Color your notebook page, *Plant Life on our Planet* to show which plants grow in various regions of our "patchwork" world.

REVIEW: 1. Why is it important to protect the rain forests? [*Protecting the rain forest helps to protect the animals and trees that live there. However, a more important issue is that God created men to be good caretakers of His creation, which includes the rain forests.*]
2. Which continent has the most rain forest area? [*South America*]
3. How does rainfall affect the type of plants that grow in an area? [*plants are uniquely adapted to the climate and soil of an area, but more plants grow where there is more rain*]
4. What regions have four seasons? [*temperate regions*]
5. Which kinds of trees can survive very cold temperatures? [*coniferous trees*]

TEST: *Student will need* **notebook p. 249,** *Crossword Review 5. Use as a review or test for older students.* **Answers:** *Teacher's p. 125.*

Have the student explain his notebook page to a friend or relative.

DIGGING DEEPER: 1. Study the types of animals that live in each climate and describe the relationship of the animals to the plant life in each zone. 2. Looking at the *Plant Life on our Planet* map, take an imaginary trip across a continent and describe the types of plants you might see. 3. How could climate zones be affected (in positive and/or negative ways) by people? (For example, the results of irrigation techniques practiced in Israel could be compared with the non-irrigated agricultural conditions in the surrounding countries.) What type of industry would be best suited for each climate zone? Why? 4. Check out Chapters 14-15 in *Lyrical Life Science, Vol. 2,* by Doug and Dorry Eldon, Lyrical Learning, 8008 Cardwell Hill, Corvallis, OR, 97330, 1996. 5. Consider the types of products that come from each type of forest (such as lumber, paper, nuts, fruits, coffee, furniture) and write a report of how they benefit the people who produce them and the people who consume them. 6. Make a list of all the wood products, including paper, in your house. Where should this wood be grown? Who should determine what types of forest management are appropriate and sustainable? 7. Compare wood to other materials—other natural fibers, metals, plastics, and minerals. Which use less energy or create less pollution? Which are renewable, recyclable, or biodegradable? Which provide biodiversity or wildlife habitat as they grown? Which cause more environmental harm in their extraction, processing and eventual disposal? 8. Research the Jari Plantations in the Amazon Basin, looking for examples of solving the problem of poverty with economic activity, as well as long-term stewardship of the tropical forest.

THE ANIMAL KINGDOM

LESSON 13: Insects

PREPARATION: *Student will need* **notebook pp. 77-81**, *crayons, scissors, glue, and pencil. Vocabulary words may be written on flash cards.*

VOCABULARY:

exoskeleton: firm outer skeleton [Gk. *exo-*, outside + *skeletos*, dried up]

insect: a large group of invertebrate animals which, in the adult stage, have three body segments, including a head, thorax, and abdomen, three pairs of legs and may have two pairs of wings [L. *in*, in + *secare*, to cut]

invertebrates: creatures without a backbone (vertebrae) [L. *in-*, not + *vertebra*, spine]

larva: the immature "baby" form of animals that changes structurally to become adult, through complete metamorphoses [L. *larva*, ghost]

metamorphosis: the process of change during the growth and development of insects [Gk. *meta*, over + *morphe* shape]

nymph: the immature form of an insect with incomplete metamorphosis [Gk. *nymphe* bride]

pupa: an insect in the non-feeding, resting stage between the larval and adult form [L. *pupa*, girl, doll]

INTRODUCTION: Out of the 1,000,000 different species of animals in the world, over 800,000 are **insects**. Every year 7,000 to 10,000 new types of insects are being discovered. Insects have done well because they can live in extreme and harsh conditions. They can live in places that are freezing as well as places that are over 120 degrees Fahrenheit, and they can eat almost anything. Though it is hard to believe, in one square mile of land there can be more insects than there are people on the whole earth. Insects are **invertebrates**. The word "invertebrates" means "creatures without backbones." Instead of a living, inner skeleton, insects have a firm outer shell called an **exoskeleton**.

The expression, "Stop bugging me" is one example of the way that many people view insects. Some insects can be irritating or downright harmful. A mosquito can disturb a good night's rest and carry deadly diseases. Hoards of locusts or ants can destroy entire fields of grain. However, only 17% of insects are harmful. Overall, insects are vital in the chain of life. They are the food eaten by birds, fish, bats, frogs, and many other animals. Pollination is one of their major jobs. Without insects, plants would be unable to produce fruit or to reproduce. Another important job is cleaning up the world by eating and decomposing (breaking down into smaller parts) dead plants and animals. This process results in several other benefits, such as halting the spread of disease and enriching the soil. In addition, insects provide us with honey, shellac, and silk.

BIBLE READING: *(Have student look up Scriptures.)* Most insects are quite small, and in the Bible, they are used to illustrate the contrast between large and small as with people (Numbers 13:33), or sins (Matthew 23:24). God used gnats, flies, and locusts to punish the Egyptians for enslaving His people (Exodus 8, 9). And the locust, cricket, and grasshopper were acceptable food for the Israelites, including John the Baptist, who ate locusts and wild honey

(Leviticus 11:22; Matthew 3:4). In the book of Proverbs, ants are given as an example of industriousness. In what ways should we be like them? (Proverbs. 6:6–8, 30:24–28) Bees are insects that provide us with honey. Honey has been treasured though the years for its sweetness. We are told that God's Word is sweeter than honey (Psalm 19:10, 119:103). If we fill our minds with too much entertainment, we'll be too full to want to read God's Word (Proverbs 27:7). Let's remember to put God first in every area of our lives.

NOTEBOOK: *Insect Detective, p. 77.* Color the insect at the top of the *Insect Detective* page. Then count the parts and write in the correct numbers on the "What makes an insect?" check list. [*Answers: 1. two antennas, 2. six legs, 3. three body sections, 4. four wings—optional, only insects have four wings but not all insects have wings.*] Now look at the animals on the rest of the page and use the check-list to help you decide whether or not they are insects. [*Answers: moth, yes; rolly-polly or sow bug, no; spider, no; beetle, yes; centipede, no; fly, yes; weevil, yes; mosquito, yes; scorpion, no.*] Now, for each animal that is an insect, color the head, thorax, and abdomen red, blue and yellow as in the example above.

The Life Cycles of Insects, pp. 78-80. Let's cut out the small boxes labeled 'a–x' from *The Life Cycles of Insects (page 2).* One of the unique characteristics of insects is that they go through different stages in their development, shedding their skins and/or changing their form as they grow. This process of change is called **metamorphosis**. The one stage that all insects have in common is the "egg" stage. Glue boxes a–d onto *The Life Cycles of Insects* page. The grasshopper gives us an example of "incomplete metamorphosis" in which the "baby" stages look very much like miniature adults. The "baby" grasshoppers, or **nymphs**, hatch from the eggs without any wings. They lose their skin several times as they grow, and add wings in the process. But they always look very much like grasshoppers. Complete metamorphosis, on the other hand, is when the "baby" or **larva** does not remotely resemble the adult and goes through a **pupa** stage before reaching adulthood. The pupa is a resting stage where the larva does not eat or move. During this time the larva's structure (except for the nervous system) completely changes. Mosquito larvae are found in stagnant water, so be careful about having water sitting around in puddles or cans around your house. You can find another type of larva (called a "grub") when you dig in the garden. Can you guess what those white grubs turn into? [*beetles*] In rotten food and dead animals you can often see white worm-like "maggots." What do you think they turn into? [*flies*]

Now, glue all the remaining boxes in the correct places on the page. Then color the insects in the boxes, and think about where each would be found. [*Answers: grasshopper, a–d; mosquito, e–h; beetle, i–l; butterfly, m–p; bee, q–t; fly, u–x.*]

Making Sense of Insects, pp. 79-81. Cut out the puzzle pieces of the grasshopper on *Making Sense of Insects (page 2)* and glue them onto the *Making Sense of Insects* page. Now see if you can figure out where the senses and functions of the grasshopper happen. Where does the grasshopper make its music (or sound)? See if you are right by looking under the windows and then write the correct letter in the box next to each body function. [*Answers: music, e; breathe, g; hear, d; heart, f; taste, c; touch, a; smell, a; see, b.*]

Now, look at the part of the page that asks, "How do these insects eat?" Insects have mouth parts that are specially adapted for the types of foods they eat. What does a mosquito eat? [*blood*]

What kind of mouth parts does a mosquito need? [*parts that will puncture the skin and suck the blood*] The mosquito has a long pointed mouth part that sticks into the skin of a person or animal and sucks out blood much like a needle and syringe work. What does a butterfly eat? [*nectar from flowers*] What kind of mouth parts does a butterfly need to stick into a flower and suck up nectar? [*parts to reach down into the flower*] The butterfly has a straw like attachment that it keeps curled up until it is needed. When this straw is unrolled, it can reach deep into flowers to suck up the nectar, much like a straw. What does a grasshopper eat? [*grass, leaves*] What kind of mouth parts does a grasshopper need? [*parts to chew with*] The grasshopper's jaws have a scissor action that helps them to chew up the grass and leaves it eats. What does a fly eat? [*decaying plant and animal material*] What kind of mouth parts does a fly need? [*parts that will absorb and suck up the material*] The fly has mouth parts that are like a funnel with a sponge attached to the end. The fly spits up a drop of gastric juice that dissolves its food and then it uses its mouth parts like a sponge to soak and suck up the digested foods.

Have you ever had trouble distinguishing a moth from a butterfly? Find some pictures of moths and butterflies (or better yet, observe some real ones). You will notice that butterflies and moths have the same general appearance but they also have some distinctive differences. When is the butterfly most active? [*The butterfly is active during the daylight hours.*] In what position does a butterfly keep its wings when it lights on a surface? [*When it lights, it keeps its wings up together.*] What kind of antennas do butterflies have? [*They have simple antennas.*] While turning from a caterpillar into a butterfly, the caterpillar forms a hard protective casing called a chrysalis.

When is the moth most active? [*As a general rule, the moth is active at night.*] In what position does a moth keep its wings when it lights on a surface? [*Its wings spread out when it is at rest.*] What do the antennas of a moth look like? [*Its antennas have a feathery appearance.*] The moth spins a fuzzy cocoon. Use the correct moth and butterfly parts on the *Making Sense of Insects* page to draw and color a butterfly and a moth in the spaces provided.

EVOLUTION STUMPERS: Ancient insects (such as ants, praying mantises, houseflies, and termites) have been preserved in petrified tree sap and were dated by some scientists to be 40–100 million years old. These insects are basically unchanged from their present day counterparts. Why didn't they develop into more complex forms? Or could it be true that creatures do reproduce "each after their own kind?"

REVIEW: 1. What are three beneficial jobs that insects do? [*pollinating plants, cleaning up dead plants and animals, making honey and silk, serving as food for animals*]
2. How can we distinguish an insect from other animals? [*they have an exoskeleton, three body segments, three pairs of legs, and often two pairs of wings*]
3. What are some different ways that insects eat? [*sucking (as a straw), piercing (as a hypodermic needle), cutting (as scissors) and soaking up (as a sponge)*]
4. What does metamorphosis mean? [*the process of change during growth and development*]
5. How does a grasshopper's metamorphosis differ from a mosquito's? [*a grasshopper goes through incomplete metamorphosis and always looks like a little grasshopper even in nymph stages, while a mosquito goes through complete metamorphosis and looks very different from the adult as it goes through pupa and larva stages*]

6. Name three differences between a moth and a butterfly. [*A moth is active at night, has feathery antennas, spreads its wings while at rest, and emerges from a fuzzy cocoon. A butterfly is active during the day, has simple antennas, keeps its wings up together, and emerges from a hard chrysalis.*]

Have the student explain his notebook page to a friend or relative and tell what he learned from the lesson. Also, review the songs/poems and activities.

DIGGING DEEPER: 1. Build an ant farm. 2. Sit outside on a warm day for 20 minutes and keep track of how many different kinds of insects you see. 3. Start an insect collection. 4. Make a bug "zoo." Keep insects in jars with holes in the lids. Find out what each one needs to live, and give them food and water. 5. Find some different types of larvae (caterpillar, grub, maggot, mosquito larvae) and watch them develop into adult insects. 6. Visit an apiary, or raise your own bees. Attend a bee-keepers' meeting. 7. Read the information related to insects in the *Character Sketches from the Pages of Scripture Illustrated in the World of Nature,* Vol. 1, 2, and 3, from the Institute in Basic Life Principles, Box 1, Oak Brook, IL 60522-3001. 8. Watch the video, *City of the Bees,* from Moody Institute of Science, 820 N. La Salle Blvd, Chicago, IL, 60610.

LESSON 14: Spiders

PREPARATION: *Student will need* **notebook p. 82** *and crayons. Vocabulary words may be written on flash cards.*

VOCABULARY:
> **arachnids:** a family of animals which have two main body parts, four pairs of legs, and which breathe with book lungs [Gk. *arachne,* a spider]
> **book lungs:** lungs characteristic of arachnids, which have tiny compartments, like the pages of a book
> **cephalothorax:** the head united with the thorax which form one section of the spider's body [Gk. *kephale,* the head + *thorax,* chest cavity]
> **spiracles:** breathing holes in the abdomen of spiders and insects, and another name for the blow hole of whales [L. *spirare,* to breathe]

INTRODUCTION: Spiders are invertebrates, but belong to a different class of animals than insects. They are **arachnids** and are related to scorpions, ticks, and horseshoe crabs. Spiders have two body parts, a **cephalothorax** (the head is united with the thorax) and an abdomen. They breathe through gill-like structures called **book lungs** which have tiny compartments that look like the pages of a book. Spiders have four pairs of legs and use the front pair somewhat like feelers. Each leg is long and thin with seven joints, and each ends in a tiny claw. This allows them to move in any direction—forward, backward, left, right, up and down. They have eight eyes.

Spiders are found everywhere and very few of them are harmful to humans. One of the most interesting things about spiders is the silk threads that they spin. A spider's silk is made of keratin and is very strong. (This is the same material that makes up fingernails, feathers and animals' horns.) If you could weave an inch-thick strand of this silk, it would be three times stronger than the same thickness of iron, and able to support 74 tons of weight. The silk can be used to capture insects for food, to provide transportation, or to spin egg sacs. Some spiders carry their egg sacs with them, and when the tiny spiders hatch, they ride on their mother's back until they are able to fend for themselves. Other spiders leave their egg sacs attached to a safe place. When a spider captures an insect in its web, it wraps it up with silk and injects it with a poison that will dissolve the insides of the victim. After awhile the spider returns to suck out the now-liquid insides of the insect, leaving only the outside crust. Some spiders, like tarantulas, can live up to twenty-five years.

BIBLE READING: *(Have student look up Scriptures.)* The web of the spider is beautiful, intricate, unique and also quite fragile. Spider webs are mentioned only twice in the Bible and are used as examples of the insecurity and godlessness of the wicked (Job 8:13-15; Isaiah 59:4-6). Why do you think would this be?

NOTEBOOK: *Caught in a Spider's Web, p. 82.* Each spider makes a distinctive web. We will be looking at the garden cross spider and the many types of silk that it can spin. The silk threads are produced from keratin, the same material that fingernails, feathers, and horns are made of. Different glands make different types of silk used for different purposes. Locate the gland pictured under number one on the spider. Draw an orange "thread" from the spider's rear to the object marked (a) to see what the thread from that gland is used for. Continue with each of the other glands.

EVOLUTION STUMPERS: Spiders make sticky webs to capture insects for food. They have oil glands on their tiny feet to keep from catching themselves in their own webs. If these evolved by natural selection, what happened to all the spider ancestors who didn't have the oil glands? Or if it was the ability to make a web that evolved by natural selection, how did the spider ancestors capture their food?

REVIEW: 1. What group do spiders belong to? [*arachnid*]
2. What are the two parts of the spider's body? [*cephalothorax and abdomen*]
3. How many types of silk threads can a garden cross spider produce? [*seven*]
4. What are some of the purposes of these different silks? [*to capture insects for food; to provide transportation; to spin egg sacs*]
5. What is the material that makes fingernails, feathers, horns, and spider's silk? [*keratin*]

TEST: *Student will need* **notebook p. 250,** *Crossword Review 6. Use as a review or test for older students.* **Answers:** *Teacher's p. 125.*

Have the student explain his notebook page to a friend or relative.

DIGGING DEEPER: 1.   Locate a spider web and watch the action for a while, especially at dusk. 2. Read *Charlotte's Web* by E.B. White. 3. Do a "string art" spider web of your own. 4. Look at the underside of rarely moved furniture for the small, round, silky egg sacs left by spiders and the dry skins of dead insects left by spiders after they have eaten. Keep an egg sac in a jar and watch the spiders hatch.

LESSON 15: Fish, Reptiles, Birds, and Mammals

INTRODUCTION: *You will be introducing four classes of animals at the same time in this lesson.* ***In future lessons, each of the four classes will be covered in greater detail and there will be notebook pages for each as well.*** *Don't worry about having the student master all of the information in this lesson at this time. There will be many more exposures.*

PREPARATION: *Color and laminate (or cover with clear sticky-backed plastic) the* Animal Classmates Game *pp. 83-88. Cut out all the cards on the dotted lines and store in an envelope or small plastic bag. Also laminate the* Features of Creatures *pp. 89-92. Cut out all the cards on the dotted lines and store in an envelope or small plastic bag. Play the games with several students, if possible.*

SONG/POEM:

Creatures God Made

Fish are cold-blooded creatures God made,
They have scales, fins, and swim in the deep,
They lay eggs, and they breathe in the water through gills,
A swim bladder helps them float while they sleep.

Reptiles are cold-blooded creatures God made,
They have dry, scaly skin and lay eggs,
Their lungs breathe the air, and their hearts have three parts,
And they crawl on their bellies or legs.

Birds are warm-blooded creatures God made,
They have feathers, two feet, and two wings,
They lay eggs, and their hearts beat the fastest of all,
And they breathe God's good air as they sing.

Mammals are warm-blooded creatures God made,
They have hair, and give milk for their young,
And whether they live on the land or the sea,
They all breathe God's air with their lungs.

ACTIVITY: *Get out the* Animal Classmates Game *cards and* Features of Creatures *cards. Shuffle the two groups of cards separately. You may need to take several days to cover this activity so that the students do not become frustrated or confused. Discuss one animal classification at a time, using the following format:*

1. *Using the* Animal Classmates *cards, lay out the large title card from the* Features of Creatures *cards for the classification to be discussed (fish, reptile, bird, mammal). Have students select the animals that go with that class and place them under the title card. Say:*
Name as many as you can. Which ones are _____? (fish, reptile, bird, mammal)

2. *Using the* Features of Creatures *cards, lay out the large title card for the class to be discussed (fish, reptile, bird, mammal). Have students select the characteristics that go with that class and*

place them under the title card. Answers are on the following chart. Say:
Let's think of some _____. (fish, reptiles, birds, mammals) What characteristics make a
_____? (fish, reptile, bird, mammal)

3. *When all of the classifications have been covered, review the definitions, and talk about the elements that each group has in common, which are most common to a particular class, which are common to a few in a particular class, and which are rare in a particular class. Use the information in the following chart.*

4. *When all of the classifications have been covered, hide the* Animal Classmates *cards around the room and divide students into three groups. One group may collect only birds, one only fish and reptiles, and one only mammals. If someone finds a card that is not in his category, he must replace it where he found it. The first group to find all 20 of their cards wins.*

Key for Features of Creatures

MAMMAL	BIRD	REPTILE	FISH
Most: backbone warm-blooded milk for babies live birth* hair/fur skin lungs legs Few: fins (whales, seals, etc.) Rare: leathery eggs (platypus and echidna) wings (bats) *Baby nourished in womb by placenta, a characteristic of only mammals (viviparous = L. vivus, living + parere, to give birth)	Most: backbone warm-blooded hard shell egg feathers lungs air sacs wings legs	Most: backbone cold-blooded leathery eggs scales leathery skin crawl on belly lungs legs Few: live birth* (some snakes) *Hatched inside the female from eggs with enclosing membranes, not nourished by a placenta (ovoviviparous = L. ovum, an egg + vivus, living + parere, to give birth)	Most: backbone cold-blooded gills air bladder jelly-like eggs fins scales Few: live birth* (guppies) skin (shark) *Hatched inside the female from eggs with enclosing membranes, not nourished by a placenta (ovoviviparous = L. ovum, an egg + vivus, living + parere, to give birth)

DIGGING DEEPER: 1. Watch the video, *Animal Kingdom*, from Moody Institute of Science, 820 N. La Salle Blvd, Chicago, IL, 60610, 1995. 4. Check out Chapters 2, 4 & 5 in Vol. 1 and Chapter 2 in Vol. 2 of *Lyrical Life Science*, by Doug and Dorry Eldon, Lyrical Learning, 8008 Cardwell Hill, Corvallis, OR 97330, 1996.

LESSON 16: Fish

PREPARATION: *Student will need **notebook pp. 94-98**, an envelope, crayons, scissors, glue, and a pencil. You will also need a small plastic bottle with a lid (that can float) and a large container of water (a sink or large bowl). Vocabulary words may be written on flash cards.*

VOCABULARY:

> **cold-blooded:** having a variable body temperature and activity level that changes according to the temperature of the surroundings
>
> **fish**: cold-blooded water animal with a backbone, fins, scales, and gills
> [O.E. *fisc*, a fish]
>
> **gills:** the breathing organ of water animals which takes oxygen out of the water
>
> **swim bladder** (air bladder): a thin-walled "sack" found in most fish which is used to enable fish to float at varying depths
>
> **vertebrates**: creatures with backbones [L. *vertebra*, spine]

INTRODUCTION: What has scales but can't weigh, goes to school but can't read, needs oxygen but can't breathe air, and can move without legs? [*Fish*!] **Fish** are the largest group of **vertebrates** (creatures with backbones). They breathe through **gills**. A fish takes water into its mouth, then forces it out through the thin gills, which contain tiny blood vessels. These blood vessels are able to take 80% of the oxygen from the water. (Water is made up of two molecules of hydrogen and one molecule of oxygen—H_2O.) Fish come in thousands of shapes, sizes and colors. Most fish have scales and fins. Their fins help them swim, turn, and balance in the water. They also have a **swim bladder** (or air bladder). By controlling the amount of air inside the swim bladder, it allows them to float at any level desired. With more air, they float higher, with less air, they settle deeper. Their amazing lateral lines (a specialized row of pores on each side of the fish) are the center for interpreting vibration and touch. Most fish reproduce by laying eggs in water. A few have eggs that hatch inside the mother so that the young are born alive (ovoviviparous). Fish have a two-chambered heart and are **cold-blooded**, so their body temperature varies, within limits, with the temperature of the water. Some fish travel in groups called "schools" while others stay by themselves. There are fish that can live in fresh water (lakes, rivers, and ponds) and others that live in salt water (oceans). Some types of fish eat plants like seaweed, while other fish eat other fish and water animals.

Let's see how the swim bladder works. First we will fill the sink (*or bowl*) with water. This will be our "ocean." Next we will take this plastic bottle, fill it all the way up with water, and put the lid on. This will be our "fish." We will put it into the water. What happens? [*It will sink.*] Now we will pour a little water out of the bottle and replace the lid. What will happen when we put it in the water this time? [*It will float near the bottom of the sink.*] Let's try again with different amounts of air in our "fish." (*Experiment with different amount of water in the bottle.*) How could a real fish stay at different depths in the ocean? [*It adjusts the amount of air in its swim bladder.*]

SONG/POEM:

Fish

Fish are cold-blooded creatures God made,
They have scales, fins, and swim in the deep,
They lay eggs and they breathe in the water through gills,
A swim bladder helps them float while they sleep.

ACTIVITY: *Review classifications by sorting the* Features of Creatures *cards as directed. Try to speed up sorting each time this is done.*

A Set of Classmates Game. Shuffle the Animal Classmates *cards and deal out five cards to each player. Leave the remaining cards face down in the middle of the table. Five animals that are in the same class make a set. The object is to collect the most sets of five. Each player takes a turn picking up a card or drawing one from another player. If the player gets a set of five, he must lay down the set and draw another card. When the player does not get a set, his turn is over.*

BIBLE READING: *(Have student look up Scriptures.)* God often uses things that He has created in unusual ways to accomplish His will. Once He provided money to pay taxes in a fish's mouth (Matthew 17:24-27). Jesus multiplied five loaves of bread and two fish into enough food to feed over five thousand people (Matthew 14:17-21). And because many of Jesus' disciples were fishermen, He called them to become "fishers of men" (Matthew 4:18-20). Jonah, however, was not so quick to follow Him. God used a large fish to swallow Jonah because he was disobedient to God. Jonah stayed in the belly of the fish for three days and three nights. Then he was willing to do what God had asked. Let's read the story of Jonah together (*at least the first three chapters of Jonah*) and then Matthew 12:39–41 to see what Jesus had to say about Jonah.

NOTEBOOK: *Word Search—FISH, p. 94.* Find the words that relate to fish and circle them. If you get stuck, look at the word bank for clues. ***Answers: Teacher's p. 122.***

Animal Detective, pp. 95-98. Cut out all the cards on the *Animal Detective (page 2)* and take out all the fish cards. Put the rest of the cards in an envelope glued to *My Animal Cards*, p. 96 to use later. Glue the fish cards in the upper right hand corner of the *Animal Detective* page. Choose a fish to study and draw a picture of it. Then fill in the *Animal Detective* page for your fish. There may be more than one answer per category.

(Cover the following information in a discussion when the page has been completed.) What is the classification for your animal; mammal, bird, fish or reptile? [*fish*] Does the animal have a backbone? [*yes*] Is it warm- or cold-blooded? [*cold-blooded*] Do the females make milk for their young? [*no*] How are the babies born? [*live birth and jelly-like egg*] What kind of covering does the animal have on its body; hair/fur, scales, skin or feathers? [*scales*] How does the animal breathe? [*gills*] How does the animal move around; with legs, wings, fins, or on its belly? [*fins*] Finally, where does the animal live? [*water*] After you have marked all your answers, color the page.

The Deep Blue Sea, pp. 99, 101-102. [You may need to work this page together with younger students.] The whole underwater world is full of creatures all designed with unique functions. There are hunters, electricity producers, shuttle buses, housecleaners, apartment complexes, farmers, cooperatives, garbage collectors and all the other things necessary for life to continue underwater. Cut out the "Fishy Facts" from *The Deep Blue Sea (page 2)* and glue them face up onto the right hand side of *The Deep Blue Sea* page. Then find out some of the fascinating facts about fish and other sea creatures by looking at the pictures and written clues to the left and find their matches in the ocean. *[You may want to read the clues aloud with the students.]* When you finish, we will read the "Fishy Facts" together and you can say the answers aloud in unison. [*Answers:* 1. *starfish;* 2. *Portuguese man-of-war;* 3. *clam;* 4. *shark;* 5. *sunfish;* 6. *sea horse;* 7. *flatfish;* 8. *great gulper fish;* 9. *porcupine fish;* 10. *anglerfish;* 11. *salmon;* 12. *Coelacanth;* 13. *flying fish.*]

EVOLUTION STUMPERS: The Coelacanth (See-la-kanth) is a fish that was supposed to have become extinct 70 million years ago. The layer of ground containing fossils of this fish was supposed to be accurately dated at 70 million years old, and evolutionists then dated anything else found with a Coelacanth fossil as being that old. However, in the 1930's and since then, as many as 30 Coelacanths have been caught alive. If it did not, as previously believed, become extinct 70 million years ago, does seeing a fossil of a Coelacanth tell us **anything at all** about the age of the rock?

REVIEW: 1. What are three characteristics of a fish? [*gills, fins, scales, swim bladder*]
2. What are some other sea creatures? [*clams, whales, Portuguese man-of-war, starfish*]
3. What does "cold-blooded" mean? [*having a variable body temperature that changes according to the surrounding temperature*]
4. Explain how fish breathe. [*They breathe through gills by taking water into their mouth, then forcing it out through the thin gills, which take 80% of the oxygen from the water.*]

Have the student explain his notebook page to a friend or relative and tell what he learned from the lesson. Also, review the songs/poems and activities.

DIGGING DEEPER: 1. Go fishing. Examine (or dissect) your catch before you cook it. 2. Find out about the three different subclasses of fish. 3. Visit an aquarium. 4. Go to a fish market (or your grocery store) and see the different kinds of sea creatures that are available. If possible, buy one whole one and examine its parts (dissect it) before you cook it. 5. Write a report on the migration of salmon. 6. Read the information related to fish in the *Character Sketches from the Pages of Scripture Illustrated in the World of Nature,* Vol. 1, 2, and 3, from the Institute in Basic Life Principles, Box 1, Oak Brook, IL 60522-3001. 7. Watch the video, *Voice of the Deep* or *Experience With an Eel,* from Moody Institute of Science, 820 N. La Salle Blvd, Chicago, IL, 60610, 1995. 8. Study other types of creatures that live in the ocean such as Echinoderms, Arthropods (Crustaceans), Mollusks, Cnidarians, and sponges. 9. Fill out a *Scientist Detective* page for Jacques-Yves Cousteau (1910-1997), well known for his study of underwater life.

LESSON 17: Reptiles

PREPARATION: *Student will need* **notebook pp. 97-98, 100, 103-106,** *scissors, glue, and crayons. Vocabulary words may be written on flash cards.*

VOCABULARY:
> **lungs**: internal, sponge-like breathing chamber of vertebrate land creatures
> [O.E. *lungen*, lung]
> **reptile**: a cold-blooded vertebrate, with lungs for breathing air, dry, scaly covering
> for body, and a three chambered heart (except for the alligator and crocodile
> which have four chambered hearts). Most live on the land and lay eggs with a
> tough, leathery shell. They crawl on their bellies or short legs. [L. *reptilis*, creeping]

INTRODUCTION: What animals do you think of when you hear the word "reptile?" [*lizards, turtles, alligators, crocodiles and snakes*] **Reptiles** are cold-blooded creatures with a well-developed backbone (vertebrate). They have **lungs** for breathing air and are covered with dry scales. Most of their time is spent on land, where they crawl on their bellies or short legs and also lay eggs with tough leathery shells. Reptiles have three-chambered hearts, except for the alligator and crocodile, which have four-chambered hearts. Reptiles generally eat insects or other animals.

SONG/POEM:

Reptiles

Reptiles are cold-blooded creatures God made,
They have dry, scaly skin and lay eggs,
Their lungs breathe the air, and their hearts have three parts,
And they crawl on their bellies or legs.

ACTIVITY: *Review classifications by sorting the* Features of Creatures *cards as directed. Try to speed up sorting each time this is done.*

It's a what? Game. Shuffle the Animal Classmates *cards and place the stack of cards face down in the middle of the table. The first player turns one card face up and sets it on the table. The next players take turns turning up the cards and placing them face up in a separate stack. If both the face up cards match classes, the first player to call out what class it belongs to (fish, reptile, bird, mammal) may collect all the face up cards. Play starts again by turning up a new card to be matched. The object is to collect the most cards.*

BIBLE READING: *(Have student look up Scriptures.)* There are many references to reptiles, particularly snakes, in the Bible. The "serpent" that tempted Eve was cursed to crawl on its belly forever after (Genesis 3:1–14). The snake then became a symbol of sin, and on one occasion God used poisonous snakes to punish the Israelites in the desert (Numbers 21). In order for them to be healed, God told Moses to make a statue of a snake out of bronze, and anyone who looked at it would be healed. This was a picture of how Jesus would take on our sins and be lifted up on a cross to heal us from our sins (John 3:14–16).

NOTEBOOK: *Word Search—REPTILES, p. 100.* Find the words that relate to reptiles and circle them. If you get stuck, look at the word bank for clues. ***Answers:*** *Teacher's p. 122.*

Animal Detective, p. 97-98, 103. Take the reptile cards from the envelope holding the *Animal Detective* cards. Glue the reptile cards in the upper right hand corner of the *Animal Detective* page. Choose a reptile you would like to study and draw a picture of it. Fill in the *Animal Detective* page for your reptile. There may be more than one answer per category. After you have marked all your answers, color the page.

(Cover the following information in a discussion when the page has been completed.) What is the classification for your animal; mammal, bird, fish or reptile? [*reptile*] Does the animal have a backbone? [*yes*] Is it warm- or cold-blooded? [*cold-blooded*] Do the females make milk for their young? [*no*] How are its babies born? [*live birth or leathery egg*] What kind of covering does the animal have on its body; hair/fur, scales, skin or feathers? [*scales or leathery skin*] How does the animal breathe? [*lungs*] How does the animal move around; with legs, wings, fins, or on its belly? [*legs or belly*] Finally, where does the animal live? [*underground, above ground, in or near water*]

Representing Reptiles, pp. 104-106. The turtle, crocodile, and rattlesnake are examples of the reptile class. On the top of the *Representing Reptiles* page, you will see how the rattlesnake strikes its victim. The poisonous fluid, or venom, that a snake injects into its victim through its fangs produces pain, swelling, inner bleeding, blood circulation problems, and death (for small animals). The rattlesnake then swallows the animal whole and digests it over several days. The crocodile has an even more interesting method of eating! You'll find out about it as you cut the pages for the snake, turtle, and crocodile from *Representing Reptiles (page 2)* and glue them onto the *Representing Reptiles* page. Finish drawing the scales on the snake and color the pictures.

REVIEW: 1. What are three examples of reptiles? [*snake, turtle, crocodile, lizard, etc.*]
2. Are reptiles warm- or cold-blooded? [*cold-blooded*]
3. Where do reptiles generally live? [*underground, above ground, near water*]
4. What do reptiles eat? [*insects and other animals*]
5. How do reptiles move? [*they crawl on their bellies or short legs*]

Have the student explain his notebook page to a friend or relative and tell what he learned from the lesson. Also, review the songs/poems and activities.

DIGGING DEEPER: 1. Visit the reptile house at a zoo. 2. Learn the different poisonous and non-poisonous snakes in your area. 3. Get a pet turtle and learn to care for it. 4. Read the information related to reptiles in the *Character Sketches from the Pages of Scripture Illustrated in the World of Nature,* Vol. 1, 2, and 3, from the Institute in Basic Life Principles, Box 1, Oak Brook, IL 60522-3001.

LESSON 18: Birds

PREPARATION: *Student will need **notebook p. 97-98, 108-109**, crayons and a pencil. Vocabulary words may be written on flash cards.*

VOCABULARY:

> **air sacs**: air-filled cavities that reach into almost every part of a bird's body, with connections to the lungs
>
> **bird**: a warm-blooded vertebrate animal, having feathers, two wings (most can fly), two legs, scaly feet, and a four-chambered heart with the fastest heartbeat of all animals. Its lungs breathe air into air sacs and hollow bones. It has no teeth, but a beak, crop, and gizzard. It reproduces by laying hard-shelled eggs. [O.E. *brid*, bird]
>
> **crop**: a sac-like enlargement in a bird's food tube, where food is stored before digesting
>
> **gizzard**: a bird's muscular second stomach, where food is ground after being partially digested in the first stomach
>
> **warm-blooded**: having the ability to maintain a constant internal body temperature

INTRODUCTION: **Birds** are the masters of the air. Other than insects and bats, no other creature is capable of true flight. Some birds can reach speeds of 100 miles per hour, which is faster than any other animal. Birds are the only creatures with feathers. Their variety and colors are truly amazing. Many have brightly colored plumage. These animals are **warm-blooded**. Their feathers, skin, and fat help insulate their bodies and keep heat in so that their internal temperature remains constant. Their fast-beating four-chambered hearts keep their bodies not just warm, but hot, with temperatures of 105 degrees to 111 degrees Fahrenheit. Many types of birds fly for hours or even days at a time, and need a constant flow of blood to their muscles. Birds have four limbs, two of which are wings, and two are legs. Their feet are covered with scales.

Birds breathe by drawing air into **air sacs**, which then pass the air to the lungs so that there is a constant flow of oxygen to the lungs. They are able to take more oxygen out of the air than any other animal. Birds have backbones and most birds have hollow bones, which makes them lighter for flight.

Not all birds fly. Some, like ostriches, run on land, and penguins swim in a flying motion through the water. Birds lay eggs, like fish and reptiles do, but their eggs have a hard shell on them. Birds have beaks, and most have no teeth. (There is a South American humming bird that does have teeth!) After they swallow their food, it can be stored in their **crop** until the stomach is ready to digest it. An organ, called the **gizzard**, grinds the partially digested food that comes from the stomach. Some birds must swallow gravel with their food to help the gizzard grind it better.

SONG/POEM:

Birds

Birds are warm-blooded creatures God made,
They have feathers, two feet, and two wings,
They lay eggs and their hearts beat the fastest of all,
And they breathe God's good air as they sing.

ACTIVITY: *Review classifications by sorting the* Features of Creatures *cards as directed. Try to speed up sorting each time this is done.*

"Yes or No" Game. *Shuffle the* Animal Classmates *cards and have one player choose a card without showing it to the other players. The other players take turns asking questions that can be answered "yes" or "no" and try to figure out what class each animal is in. Three questions must be asked before asking the specific class. Questions should use the characteristics from the* Features of Creatures *Game (e.g., "Does it have skin?" and so forth). The player who guesses the correct class is the next to choose an animal card. If there are several players, teams may be formed.*

BIBLE READING: *(Have student look up Scriptures.)* God used ravens as His servants to provide food for Elijah (1 Kings 17:2-6). Noah sent a dove out of the ark to see if land had appeared (Genesis 8:8-12). Jesus used birds as examples many times in His teachings. He told us to be as wise as serpents and as innocent as doves (Matthew 10:16). Jesus reminded us that birds don't plant or harvest, but God feeds them (Matthew 6:25–26; Luke 12:24). In spite of how small and insignificant sparrows seem, Jesus told us that not one sparrow falls without God being aware of it. Then He says that we are of more value than many sparrows (Matthew 10:29–31). What do you worry about? God says that there is nothing that can separate us from His love (Romans 8:35–39).

NOTEBOOK: *Word Search—BIRDS, p. 108.* Find the words that relate to birds and circle them. If you get stuck, look at the word bank for clues. **Answers:** *Teacher's p. 122.*

Animal Detective, p. 97-98, 109. We will be filling out an *Animal Detective* page for a bird today. Take the bird cards from the envelope holding the *Animal Detective* cards. Glue the bird cards in the upper right hand corner of the *Animal Detective* page. Choose a bird you would like to study and draw a picture of it. Then fill in the *Animal Detective* page for your bird. There may be more than one answer per category. After you have marked all your answers, color the page.

(Cover the following information in a discussion when the page has been completed.) What is the classification for your animal; mammal, bird, fish or reptile? [*bird*] Does the animal have a backbone? [*yes*] Is it warm- or cold-blooded? [*warm-blooded*] Do the females make milk for their young? [*no*] How are the babies born? [*hard shell egg*] What kind of covering does the animal have on its body; hair/fur, scales, skin or feathers? [*skin, feathers*] How does the animal breathe? [*air sacs*] How does the animal move around; with legs, wings, fins, or on its belly? [*legs, wings*] Finally, where does the animal live? [*sky, above ground, trees*]

REVIEW: 1. What characteristics distinguish birds from other animals? [*feathers, wings, crop, gizzard, and air sacs*]
2. What characteristics help birds to be able to fly? [*hollow bones, air sacs, wings*]
3. How do birds digest their food? [*food is stored in the crop and then ground in gizzard*]

Have the student explain his notebook page to a friend or relative and tell what he learned from the lesson. Also, review the songs/poems and activities.

DIGGING DEEPER: 1. Become a "Birder." Keep track of every kind of bird you see and attend a Bird Watchers' Meeting. 2. Find several bird nests and watch for the kind of birds that come to them. 3. Incubate a chicken or duck egg and watch it hatch. 4. Start a feather collection. 5. In an encyclopedia, look for birds that do not fly. 6. Draw and write a report about your state bird. 7. Read the information related to birds in the *Character Sketches from the Pages of Scripture Illustrated in the World of Nature,* Vol. 1, 2, and 3, from the Institute in Basic Life Principles, Box 1, Oak Brook, IL 60522-3001. 8. Fill out a *Scientist Detective* page on James Audubon (1785-1851) and find some of his paintings of birds.

LESSON 19: Mammals

PREPARATION: *Student will need **notebook p. 97-98, 110-111,** crayons and a pencil. Vocabulary words may be written on flash cards.*

VOCABULARY:
> **diaphragm**: the muscles dividing the chest cavity from the abdominal cavity [Gk. *dia*, through + *phragma*, fence]
> **mammal**: a warm-blooded vertebrate covered with fur or hair, breathing air with lungs and a diaphragm, having a four-chambered heart, and the largest and most developed brains. The female has glands that produces milk to feed her young, and most give birth to live young (viviparous). [L. *mamma*, mother, breast]
> **marsupial**: a group of mammals in Australia which give birth to incompletely developed young, and then care for them several months in an external pouch [Gk. *marsypion*, pouch, bag]
> **placenta**: an organ of blood vessels that supply food and air exchange for the babies developing inside female mammals [Gk. *plakounta*, a flat cake]

INTRODUCTION: *(Write "lion", "dog", "camel", and "whale" on the blackboard.)* What do a lion, a dog, a camel, and a whale have in common? [*They are all mammals.*] What does this mean? Do they live in the same kinds of places? [*no*] Do they eat the same foods? [*no*] Do they all breathe air? [*yes*] **Mammals** all draw air into their lungs with the help of the **diaphragm**, the muscle above their stomach and below their lungs. What kind of covering do these four animals have? [*They have fur, except for the whale, which has a few whiskers.*] Would their bodies feel warm or cold? [*warm*] Yes. Mammals are warm-blooded animals with an efficient four-chambered heart and thick covering of fat, skin, and hair or fur to keep in their body heat. Why do you think a dog can be trained to do tricks and that the whale can communicate through long songs with its companions in the water? [*They are intelligent; they have well-developed brains.*] Mammals have brains that are larger and more developed than those of other animals and they have backbones. However, the features that truly distinguish mammals from other animals are the ways that they give birth and nourish their young. Most mammal females carry their young inside their bodies until they are fully developed and ready to be born. These are called "placental" mammals because a **placenta** (an organ full of blood vessels) nourishes the baby in its mother's womb. (They are also called "viviparous," meaning "live birth.") Several of the mammals in Australia, however, are **marsupials**, which give birth before the young are fully developed. The females then carry these tiny babies in a special pouch and feed them milk from nipples in the pouch, until they are fully developed. All female mammals have a gland that produces milk to feed their young. Two kinds of mammals lay leathery eggs, but then they feed milk to their young once they hatch (platypus and echidna, both from Australia). There are fewer types of mammals than any other group of animals, but there are still hundreds of different kinds of mammals.

SONG/POEM:

Mammals

Mammals are warm-blooded creatures God made,
They have hair, and give milk to their young,
And whether they live on the land or the sea,
They all breathe God's air with their lungs.

ACTIVITY: *Review classifications by sorting the* Features of Creatures *cards as directed. Try to speed up sorting each time this is done.*

Match a Pair Game. Select 6 animals from each classification of the Animal Classmates *cards. Shuffle these cards and place them all face down in the middle of the table in rows of six across and four down. The first player turns up two cards at a time. If the classification matches, he may keep them and turn up two more until he turns up two cards that do not match. These two are then turned face down again, and the next player takes his turn. The object is to collect the most cards.*

NOTEBOOK: *Word Search— MAMMALS, p. 110.* Find the words that relate to mammals and circle them. Look at the word bank for clues. *Answers: Teacher's p. 122.*

Animal Detective, p. 97-98, 111. We will be filling out an *Animal Detective* page for a mammal today. Take the mammal cards from the envelope holding the *Animal Detective* cards. Glue the mammal cards in the upper right hand corner of the *Animal Detective* page. Choose a mammal you would like to study and draw a picture of it. Then fill in the *Animal Detective* page for your mammal. There may be more than one answer per category. After you have marked all your answers, color the page.

(Cover the following information in a discussion when the page has been completed.) What is the classification for your animal; mammal, bird, fish or reptile? [*mammal*] Does the animal have a backbone? [*yes*] Is it warm- or cold-blooded? [*warm-blooded*] Do the females make milk for their young? [*yes*] How are the babies born? [*live birth or, rarely, leathery eggs*] What kind of covering does the animal have on its body; hair/fur, scales, skin or feathers? [*skin, hair/ fur*] How does the animal breathe? [*lungs*] How does the animal move around; with legs, wings, fins, or on its belly? [*legs, or rarely, wings*] Finally, where does the animal live? [*above ground, underground, water, trees*]

BIBLE READING: *(Have student look up Scriptures.)* Many mammals are mentioned in the Bible. Sheep, however, are mentioned the most often. Shepherds tended their sheep carefully (1 Samuel 17:34-36), looked for them when they got lost (Luke 15:4-7), and had such a close relationship with them, that the sheep knew their voice (John 10:3-5). Jesus described Himself as the "Good Shepherd", who was willing even to die protecting His sheep (John 10:11-18). Psalm 23 is a beautiful picture of how God takes care of us, His sheep. Let's recite it together.

EVOLUTION STUMPERS: The evolution of the horse is often presented on evolutionary charts in a simple, seemingly straight-forward manner. The drawings are arranged in the supposed order of evolution from the smallest to the largest. However, two or more different types from the "horse series" have been found buried in the same layer of rock. In addition, no one mentions that the ribs of the animals in the series "progress" from 18 pairs to 15 pairs to 19 pairs and back down to the present day 18 pairs. Does that make good evolutionary sense?

REVIEW: 1. What are three characteristics unique to mammals? [*female provides milk for young, live birth (placental), skin (hair/fur), most intelligent*]
2. Name five mammals. [*dog, cat, hamster, horse, cow, sheep, whale, and so forth*]
3. What are marsupials? [*Australian mammals, such as kangaroos, which give birth before the young are fully developed, then carry them in a pouch*]
4. What are two clues that would help you figure out where an animal lives? [*many possible answers including color or thickness of fur, ability to climb, shape of feet or hooves*]

Have the student explain his notebook page to a friend or relative and tell what he learned from the lesson. Also, review the songs/poems and activities.

DIGGING DEEPER: 1. Visit the zoo and see mammals from other countries. 2. Write a report on mammals in your state or country. 3. With adult supervision, cut a very small sample of fur or hair from as many types of mammals as you can (dogs, cats, hamsters, horses, cows, sheep, and so forth). Then tape the samples on a page and label which animal each came from. If possible, look at each under a microscope. 4. Get a mammal for a pet. Write down how to care for it. If possible, get a female who may bear young, so that you can observe the process of live birth. 5. Visit a veterinarian. Before your visit, write out questions that you would like to ask. 6. Write a report on Australian marsupials. 7. Read the information related to mammals in the *Character Sketches from the Pages of Scripture Illustrated in the World of Nature*, Vol. 1, 2, and 3, from the Institute in Basic Life Principles, Box 1, Oak Brook, IL, 60522-3001.

LESSON 20: My Zoo Adventure

PREPARATION: *Student will need* **notebook pp. 113-129**, *crayons and a pencil. You will need several pictures of zoo animals, preferably in their natural environment. If at all possible, a follow-up trip to the zoo should be planned. Vocabulary words may be written on flash cards.*

VOCABULARY:
habitat: dwelling, home [L. *habitare*, to dwell]

INTRODUCTION: God made animals to be able to survive in almost every nook and cranny of the world. Each animal has special characteristics that allow it to survive where God placed it. By knowing some basic facts, you will be able to make some "educated" guesses about where an animal lives, what it eats, and some of its special needs. Let's go over some things that we can figure out by observation and deduction.

ACTIVITY: *(Choose several pictures of zoo animals in their natural habitat from magazines, encyclopedias, or books.)* By looking at these pictures, we can tell a lot about the needs of an animal. Let's go over several of them together so that you will learn how to make good observations.

Use the following charts to ask thought-provoking questions about various animals. For example, say, "If you see an animal in a tropical forest, what kind of climate is it used to?" [a tropical forest has rain and sun] "Where would you expect to find an animal with a layer of fat, wide feet or hooves, and well-insulated with fur?" [polar] "Can you name some of the animals from this category?" [polar bear, penguins, caribou, seals, and so forth] "If an animal had sharp claws and teeth, what would it probably eat?" [meat] Continue with questions selected from each chart. You may want to spread this out over several days.

Climate. Question: If the animal lives in _____, then what is the probable climate?

If the animal lives in:	then what is the probable climate?
deciduous forest	rain, snow, sun
rain forest	rain, sun
grasslands	sun, wind
desert	sun, wind (snow)
polar	snow, wind
swamp	rain, sun
ocean	rain, wind, sun
mountains	rain, snow, sun, wind

Habitat (**Where does it live?**). **Question:** If the animal has _____, then where will it probably live?

If the animal has:	then where will it probably live?
very thick fur, thick layer of fat or well insulated with feathers	polar
large ears	desert
wide feet or hooves	desert or polar
climbing body, long arms and legs, grasping tails	forest
little or no need to drink water	desert
thick fur and rock climbing ability	mountains
long legs	grasslands
swimming ability	swamp or ocean
second eyelid	water or sand
white or gray-blue color	most polar
sandy colored	most desert
khaki colors	most grasslands
stripes	most grasslands
spots	forest

Diet. Question: If the animal has/is *(or lives in)* _____, then what will it probably eat?

If the animal has/is (or lives in):	then what will it probably eat?
long legs and/or chewing teeth	grass and leaves
climbing, reaching hands	leaves, fruit, seeds
small pointed beak	bugs
round hooked beak	nuts
sharp claws and teeth	meat
hooked beak (not rounded)	meat
super sharp eyes	meat
a large sized animal	fruit, leaves, grass
a very small animal	bugs or seeds
a large sea animal	fish (except baleen whales)
a night flyer	bugs, small animals, fruit
grasslands	grass or bugs
trees	leaves, bugs, or fruit

Shelter. Question: If the animal lives in *(or has)* _____, then where will its home probably be?

If the animal lives in (or has):	then where will its home probably be?
grasslands	open or tunnels
water	nest or open (some tunnels)
forest trees	nest, tree holes
forest floor	tunnels, caves, open
mountains	often caves
digging feet	tunnels

Special Needs. Question: If the animal lives in *(or is)* _____, what may be some of its needs?

If the animal lives in (or is):	what are its needs?
large groups	friends
tunnels	dirt
dry or warm climates	storm house, climate control
trees	climbing tree
water	accessible water
caves or mountains	rocks
very cold climate	climate control
forest	bushes
a grass eater	fields of grass
a solitary or night animal	privacy

NOTEBOOK: *My Zoo Adventure* and *Zoo Creatures pp. 113-129 (Although this portion is designed for a real trip to the zoo, it can also be done in the classroom.)* When was the last time you went to a zoo? The purpose of a zoo is to allow us to see animals first hand from places that we might never have a chance to visit. In the most successful zoos, every effort is made to make things as close as possible to each animal's natural **habitat**. What kinds of things would you have to do for an animal if you were their zookeeper? Let's learn more about this today. *(Note: You may want to have the students make a "zoo", adding the animals only after they have filled out a* My Zoo Adventure Book *page for them. See the "Digging Deeper" section, #1 and #2, for ideas on how to set up a zoo.)*

Choose an animal that you would like to study for your zoo. Draw a picture of it on the back of the *My Zoo Adventure Book* page. Now let's fill out the *My Zoo Adventure* page with information about this particular animal. You may have to guess some of the information, but try to make an "educated" guess! *(Do at least two animals from each category.)* What is the name of the animal? What is its class? Look closely at the animal. What does its body structure and covering tell you about the climate this animal would come from? If you have a picture of the animal, look at the background in the picture. With the clues we can get from the animal itself, where do you think this animal lives? Mark and color the closest choice. What can you tell about the animal from its color? Animals usually blend in with their habitat (where they live). Mark and color the closest choice. What kind of mouth parts (or beak) does your animal have? Does it have claws for digging or grasping? What kind of diet (food) do you think your animal eats? Mark and color the closest choice. What kind of home does your animal normally live in? In a nest? A tunnel? The water? Mark and color the closest choice. Now consider the special needs of your animal. If you took your animal away from where it normally lives, what kind of special things would you need to provide for it in your zoo? Would it need to live in a place with a constant temperature? Would it need dirt or rocks? Would it have to have friends to be content? If you aren't sure of some of your answers, check them out in an encyclopedia. Then choose another animal to study in the same way. Draw its picture on the preceding *Zoo Creatures* page in your notebook. *(Encourage the student to analyze and observe before looking up the animal information in a reference book.)*

DIGGING DEEPER: 1. Make a "zoo" out of sticks and clay. You may only add animals after you have figured out their needs from filling out your *Zoo Adventure* page. Be sure that your zoo fits the needs of your animals. 2. Do the same as #1, but make a mural on a large piece of paper instead of using sticks and clay. 3. Compare three mammals, showing how each functions perfectly for where it lives (e.g., the camel, the polar bear, and the sloth). 4. Arrange for a specially guided tour of the "behind the scenes" at a nearby zoo. 5. Watch the video, *Prior Claim*, from Moody Institute of Science, 820 N. La Salle Blvd, Chicago, IL, 60610, 1995.

LESSON 21: Amphibians

PREPARATION: *Student will need **notebook pp. 130-132**, crayons, scissors, glue, and a pencil. Vocabulary words may be written on flash cards.*

VOCABULARY:
>**amphibian:** a cold-blooded vertebrate that hatches and develops in the water, breathing with gills, and then changes to an air-breathing land animal as an adult [Gk. *amphi*, on both sides + *bios*, life]
>**hibernation:** dormant or inactive state, especially as in winter [L. *hibernare*, fr. *hiems*, winter]
>**estivation:** a state of inactivity, especially during dry summer [l. *aestus*, summer]

INTRODUCTION: Do you remember the word we learned when we studied how insects develop from an egg to an adult? [*metamorphosis*] **Amphibians** are a class of animals that also go through the process of metamorphosis. The word "amphibian" means "double life." These cold-blooded creatures are very different as adults than when they were young. Most of the amphibians hatch from eggs that have been laid in the water. They have gills (like fish) and live in the water until they change into adults. As adults, they breathe air with lungs (like reptiles) and often live on land. There are several types of amphibians. Caecilians are limbless and look like worms. A salamander may look like a lizard, but it is not. Salamanders start out their lives in the water, without legs and with gills. Then they grow four legs, with the front legs growing first. They keep their tails and their skin must always be moist. Some salamanders never leave the water, while others return to it in later life. The giant salamander of Japan grows to be five feet long and weighs up to 100 pounds!

Frogs and toads are another group of amphibians. They hatch in the water from jelly-like eggs into tadpoles. As tadpoles, they have smooth, wet skin, tails, fins, and gills. The tadpoles have small sucking mouths and a long digestive tract, which is necessary for digesting the algae that they eat. As they grow, their tails shrink, they grow legs and develop lungs. More than just these visible changes occur as well. Their digestive tracts change and they acquire a wide jaw and a long sticky tongue to catch and eat insects. They leave the water, but must stay moist since they breathe through their skin. Frogs and toads bury themselves in mud and become inactive in the cold winter and in the hot, dry summer. In the winter, this is called **hibernation**, while in the summer it is called **estivation**.

SONG/POEM:
>**Amphibians**
>Amphibians are cold-blooded creatures God made
>They lay eggs and in water are hatched,
>But when they grow up their gills into lungs change
>And damp land then becomes their new range.

BIBLE: Do you recall the story of the ten plagues God sent to the Egyptians when the Pharaoh would not let the Israelites leave? A plague is a punishment for doing something wrong. God says that we should not worship anything or anyone but Him (Deuteronomy 5:6–9). However, the ancient Egyptians worshipped many gods, including the god of the sun, moon, the Nile River, and numerous animals, including the frog. Each of the plagues were related in some way to the gods that the Egyptians worshipped, and was to show them that the true God, the Creator, was incredibly more powerful than anything in His creation. He is the one to be worshipped and not His creation. Let's read about the plague of the frogs in Exodus 8:1–15. If God sent plagues to our country today to turn people back to Himself, what kind of plagues do you think He might send? What are some of the things that we worship as a nation? Can you think of any events that you have heard about that might be punishments for our country? God promises that if we will turn from wrongdoing and seek to obey and worship Him, He will heal our land (2 Chronicles 7:13–14).

NOTEBOOK: *Amphibian Detective, pp. 130-132.* Amphibians are distinctive for their "double lives." Complete the drawings, then color, cut, fold, and glue the booklet from the *Amphibian Detective (page 2)* onto the top left corner of the *Amphibian Detective* page. When you finish, mark the characteristics of tadpoles and adult frogs.

EVOLUTION STUMPERS: One of the important laws of science is called the Second Law of Thermodynamics, which states simply, that everything moves from more order to less order. If you think of your bedroom, you can see this happening. When you straighten up the room on Saturday, by Wednesday, if you are there and don't straighten it up again, it is less orderly than it was the day before. If this concept is applied to evolution, how can a one-celled amoebae develop into all other forms of life, each of which are increasingly more complex and orderly than the one before?

REVIEW: 1. Name three amphibians. [*caecilians, salamanders, newts, frogs, toads*]
2. What does the word "amphibian" mean? [*double life*]
3. What are three differences between a tadpole and an adult frog? [*a tadpole lives in water, breathes with gills, eats algae, and swims with a tail; a frog lives on land, breathes air, eats insects, and hops with legs*]
4. What are two similarities between a tadpole and an adult frog? [*both are vertebrates and cold-blooded*]

TEST: *Student will need **notebook p. 251**, Crossword Review 7. Use as a review or test for older students. **Answers:** Teacher's p. 126.*

Have the student explain his notebook page to a friend or relative.

DIGGING DEEPER: 1. Catch some tadpoles, keep them in a glass dish with shallow water and flat rocks, feed them with bread crumbs and watch them develop into frogs. 2. Do a report on the different types of amphibians. 3. Find a book on "origami" and learn to fold a paper frog.

ANIMAL ANATOMY & PHYSIOLOGY

LESSON 22: Animal Structure

PREPARATION: *Color the paper of the* Animal Tracks Game. ***pp. 143-148**, brown. Then, laminate the pages (or cover with clear sticky-backed plastic) and cut on the dotted lines. Student will need **notebook pp. 133, 135-142, 149-156**, scissors, crayons, a pencil, glue, and if possible, feathers (for* Flight *page). Vocabulary words may be written on flash cards.*

VOCABULARY:

antlers: a bony structure growing on the head of male deer
[L. *ante*, before + *oculus*, the eye]

horns: a hard formation growing on the head of some goats, cows, and other animals
[O.E., *horn*, horn]

ligaments: strong bands of tissues that hold bones together [L. *ligare*, to bind]

muscles: a band of fibrous tissue which can produce movement

paleontologist: someone who studies plant and animal life of ancient times
(the fossil record) [Gk. *palaios*, ancient + *logos*, discourse, word]

skeleton: the framework of the body [Gk. *skeletos*, dried up]
[L. *musculus*, a muscle]

INTRODUCTION: The framework that gives animals their shape is their **skeleton**. Vertebrates, or animals with backbones, have skeletons inside their bodies. By way of contrast, when the skeleton is outside the body (like insects and spiders), it is called an exoskeleton. We often forget that bones are alive; that they are actually living tissue which can even repair themselves when they are broken. Besides providing support for the body, bones also protect the delicate inner parts of the body. The skull is like a helmet that protects the brain, the ribs protect the heart and lungs, and the backbone (spinal column) is fantastically arranged to allow movement as well as to protect the spinal cord. In addition, bones also produce new red blood cells that are formed in the marrow (or middle) of the long bones. When bones are not used, they deteriorate and become weaker because they lose calcium. Bones are held together with **ligaments** and are attached to **muscles** so that the animals can move. Muscles often come in matched pairs; extensor muscles for straightening or extending outward, and flexor muscles for bending or flexing upward. The way the skeleton and muscles work together affects how an animal moves and lives. Here is a song about how a footprint can tell us where an animal lives and how it moves.

SONG/POEM:

You'll Know Them by Their Footprints
How can you tell there's a rabbit around,
Just by looking at the ground?
How can you tell that a bird's nearby,
Without ever looking at the sky?

You'll know it by their footprints and there's more,
By where they walk and what they live for.
You'll know them by their footprints,
You'll know them by their footprints.

How can you tell that a skunk's been there,
Just by smelling of the air?
How can you tell that a bear was here,
But that he's long gone and there's no need to fear?

You'll know it by their footprints and there's more,
By where they walk and what they live for.
You'll know them by their footprints,
You'll know them by their footprints.

How can they know that a Christian passed by,
Without a word and without a sigh?
How can they know there's a better place,
Before they see Jesus face to face?

They'll know us by our footprints and what's more,
By where we walk and what we live for.
They'll know us by our footprints,
They'll know us by His footprints.

BIBLE READING: *(Have student look up Scriptures.)*   Much of what we know about the past is from evidence that remains behind, such as bones, impressions, footprints, and other fossil remains. And trackers are very good about knowing what animal has gone by, how long ago it was there, and how fast it was traveling. The Bible has a lot to say about feet and footprints as well. God's word is like a light to our feet (Psalm 119:105). Feet have special duties (Habakkuk 3:19; Romans 10:15) and our feet should be specially prepared for these assignments (John 13:5–16; Ephesians 6:13–18). If we were to have been a day behind Jesus everywhere He went when He was on this earth, what evidence would we have about Him? Let's read as much as we can of the gospel of John and look for some of the signs that Jesus would have left behind. What kind of footprints we are leaving behind with our lives?

NOTEBOOK: *A Pile of Bones, pp. 133, 135-136. (This is a difficult page for younger children. Unless you have lots of time and patience, skip it for now.)* Pretend you are a **paleontologist**, [pay lee on **taw** luh jist] someone who studies animal life in ancient times by piecing together their remaining bones. You have just discovered a pile of modern day bones and now it is up to you to figure out what kind of animal they each belong to. Color and cut out the bones on *A Pile of Bones (page 2)*, then glue them in the correct places on the *A Pile of Bones* page. Then color the bottom of the page as directed.

Horns and Antlers, pp. 135-138. Several animals, like deer, cows, and goats, have hard growths on their heads. How can we tell which of these growths are horns and which are antlers? **Horns** have a bony core and are kept throughout the animal's lifetime, growing a small amount each year. **Antlers**, on the other hand, grow only on male members of the deer family and are shed every year in the fall. Each spring, the skin-covered antler grows back with more branches, or points. Antlers are the fastest growing bone in nature. When the antler is mature, the velvety covering comes off and the nerves and blood circulation are shut off also. Color and cut out the pieces from the *Horns and Antlers* (page 2) and place them as directed on the *Horns and Antlers* page.

Flight and *Birds in Flight, pp. 139-142.* [*Cut out the* Birds in Flight *and glue or staple together in reverse order on the* Flight *page. Then follow directions for the rest of the* Flight *page.* **When the page is completed, use the following information for a discussion.**]

It takes an amazing interplay of almost every aspect of a bird's structure to enable it to fly. God created the feather to be a very complex yet lightweight structure. What makes up a feather? [*Each feather has a shaft with hundreds of thousands of barbs, hooks, and hooklets.*] Birds spend a lot of time pruning, that is cleaning and keeping their feathers in top shape. With its beak, a bird combs its feathers, putting pressure on all the barbs, hooks, and hooklets so that they go together into a smooth flat surface. Each fits together, much like the two sides of a zipper interlock, making the feather a perfect airfoil. Over time, the feathers break and start to get worn out. Since these feathers must be in top condition, most birds molt, that is lose their flight feathers, once a year. During this time they cannot fly and must be in a protected place until these feathers grow back. Other feathers help keep birds warm. These downy feathers are close to the bird's body and serve as a blanket.

Birds also have the most efficient breathing system of any animal. They are able to get the most oxygen out of the air. What helps birds to have a constant flow of oxygen through their lungs? [*nine air sacs*] Why do you think it would be important for birds to have such an efficient breathing system? [*Because this enables birds to fly at great altitudes where the air is thin and has a low level of oxygen.*] One bird, the barhead goose, flies in the very thin air over the highest mountain ranges in the world, the Himalayas, at heights of over 25,000 feet or close to 5 miles high.

What is it about the bird's bone structure that enables it to fly? [*In order to be lightweight, they are hollow.*] What do you think makes these hollow bones strong enough to hold up and support the bird in its daily activities? [*They are reinforced with struts and braces.*] Airplane wings are made like this—with struts and braces. It is the best possible structure in order to be both lightweight and sturdy.

Can you guess what other function hollow bones serve? [*Air can enter the bones from the air sacs and help cool the bird's temperature.*] Since birds do not sweat, beating the wings for hours and days would build up too much heat if they could not cool off. The air sacs are connected to the hollow bones and together they cool the bird from the inside.

The bird's breastbone, or the sternum, is the largest of any animal in proportion to its size. This bone is where the muscles for flight are attached. In preparation for long flights, birds must eat almost continually during their waking hours. They digest food more quickly and more thoroughly than other animals.

EVOLUTION STUMPERS: Birds are supposed to have evolved from reptiles according to the charts of evolution. The scales of a lizard supposedly grew long and frayed into "feathers." It is curious that there is no fossil record of any partially developed feathers. If the earth is millions of years old, and millions of animals have lived and died during this time, there should be thousands of examples of the various stages of development. Where are the fossils of these frayed scales and how could a scale fray into such an elaborate, delicate, and finely crafted aerodynamic structure as a feather?

ACTIVITY: Cut out *My Animal Tracks Book, pp. 149-152* on the dotted lines and put together in order. [*You may make a cover out of construction paper if desired.*] Fold in half. Staple at center-fold. [*Older students may draw the footprints from the examples in* My Animal Tracks Book (page 2), *p. 151, on the blank page across from each animal. Younger students may cut out and glue the individual tracks to the appropriate pages.*] Keep this book for the *Animal Tracks Game* and also to glue on the *Locomotion* page when you are finished using it.

[*Get out the* Animal Tracks Game *cards. To play this game, have someone go ahead on a trail in a wooded area and make the following preparations. Place a set of footprints on the ground, weighing them down with a stone or sticks. With clear cellophane tape, tape the corresponding animal to a tree or rock within ten feet of the footprint. (Caution: Be sure to put the animal in plain view. The animals are easily lost if hidden too well.) When preparations are complete, have the students go over the trail with their* My Animal Tracks Book *in hand. They are to find a footprint and look around until they see the animal. Then they are to write the number of the animal in their book by the footprint. The last person in line can pick up the animal and the footprint. (Note: If a wooded area is unavailable, adapt the game to your home, classroom, gymnasium, or yard.)*]

Locomotion and *Horse in Motion, pp. 153-156.* Color, cut and assemble the flip chart from *Horse in Motion* page to glue on the *Locomotion* page. Also glue the *My Animal Tracks Book* in place when you have finished using it for the ACTIVITY.

REVIEW: 1. What are three purposes for bones? [*serve as the framework for body; protection; production of red blood cells*]
2. What are two differences between horns and antlers? [*horns have a bony core and grow slowly throughout an animal's lifetime; antlers are fast-growing bone, grow only on male deer, and are shed each year*]
3. How are a bird's bones different from other animals? [*they are hollow, with struts and braces*]
4. What special structures allow birds to fly? [*wings, air sacs, and hollow bones*]
5. What are some things that you can tell about an animal from its footprints? [*what kind of animal it was, how long ago it was there, and how fast it was going*]

Have the student explain his notebook page to a friend or relative and tell what he learned from the lesson. Also, review the songs/poems and activities.

DIGGING DEEPER: 1. Write a research paper about the history of the airplane and note what part birds played in its development. 2. Collect some different types of bones from a chicken, a cow, and a fish (from a butcher shop) and compare them. 3. Cut up a chicken (for supper) with adult assistance and look at its ligaments, cartilage, muscles, and bones. 4. Summarize, in an outline form, the preparation and requirements needed to become a veterinarian. 5. Go on a camp-out or outing and make plaster of paris casts of animal footprints you find.

LESSON 23: Animal Food Chain

PREPARATION: *Student will need **notebook pp. 157-176**, crayons, scissors, glue, and a pencil. Vocabulary words may be written on flash cards.*

VOCABULARY:
>**carnivore:** meat-eater [L. *carnis*, flesh + *vorare*, to devour]
>**ecosystem**: balanced relationship between the plants and animals in a given area
>>[Gk. *ekloge*, a house + L. *systema*, organized whole]
>**herbivore:** plant-eater [L. *herva*, grass + *vorare*, to devour]
>**nutrient:** something that nourishes [L. *nutrire*, to nourish]
>**omnivore:** plant- and animal-eater [L. *omnis*, all + *vorare*, to devour]

INTRODUCTION: Every living thing needs energy to survive. As you have already studied, plants are able to make their own food by the process of photosynthesis. Animals, however, must rely on plants or other animals for their food. There is a circle of relationships in this food chain, and each animal, from the largest to the smallest, plays an important part in it. An **ecosystem** is the delicate balanced relationship between the plants and animals in a given area. (For example, if you cut down too many trees in an area, you take away shelter, food and protection from the animals and plants that were living in that area.)

Once food is eaten, the animal's digestive system breaks it down into very small parts known as **nutrients**. Then the intestines absorb these nutrients, which enter the bloodstream and are carried to every part of the body. The parts of the food that are not needed are passed out of the body as waste. Water is essential for digesting as well as for distributing the nutrients.

SONG/POEM:
>**What if the Sun Shut Down?**
>What if the sun shut down?
>What would we all do then?
>The plants could not make food
>It would be the living end.
>There would be no vegetables, no fruits, no grass, no grains, no wheat,
>And then no cows, no milk, no chickens, no eggs, no meat.
>We need the sunshine. Thank God for the sunshine.
>We need the sunshine. Thank God for the sunshine.
>
>What if the sea dried up?
>What would we all do then?
>The plants could not make food.
>It would be the living end.

There would be no vegetables, no fruits, no grass, no grains, no wheat,
And then no cows, no milk, no chickens, no eggs, no meat.
We need the water. Thank God for the water.
We need the water. Thank God for the water.

What if the air went bad?
What would we all do then?
The plants could not make food.
It would be the living end.
There would be no vegetables, no fruits, no grass, no grains, no wheat,
And then no cows, no milk, no chickens, no eggs, no meat.
We need the atmosphere. Thank God for the atmosphere.
We need the atmosphere. Thank God for the atmosphere.

Someday this world will end,
A new one will take its place.
Old things will pass away.
We'll see Jesus face to face.
We won't need no vegetables, no fruits, no grass, no grains, no wheat,
Won't need no cows, no milk, no chickens, no eggs, no meat.
We just need Jesus. Thank you, God, for Jesus.
We just need Jesus. Thank you, God, for Jesus.

BIBLE READING: *(Have student look up Scriptures.)*   From the beginning, God has provided for the needs of all His creation and all creation should praise Him. Let's read about this together in Psalm 104 and 148.

NOTEBOOK: *What Percent is Water? p. 157.* Water is in everything that is alive. All animals and plants have some water in them. Some animals, especially desert animals, get all the water they need from leaves and seeds. Water is essential for life. It helps to distribute nutrients and oxygen to each part of all living things and also plays an important part in carrying away the wastes. If an animal or person loses too much water (through sweating, diarrhea, and vomiting), they become dehydrated and could die. This page will give you a comparison of how much water is in different forms of life. Color in the percent of water for each object.

Beaks and Feet Show Where Birds Live and What They Eat, pp. 159-162. You can tell a lot about where birds live and what kind of food they eat just by looking at their beaks and their feet. Glue the *Beaks and Feet Show Where Birds Live and What They Eat (page 2)* onto the bottom of the page. Use the information there to figure out what the beaks and feet of each bird show. Then write in the answers on the lines provided. [***Answers****: Toucan— eat fruit, perch; Parrot—crack nuts, perch; Eagle—tear prey, grasp prey; Robin—trap insects, perch; Humming Bird—sip nectar, perch; Ostrich—eat leaves, run; Woodpecker—chisel wood, climb; Flamingo—strain mud, walk on water lilies; Kiwi Bird—probe, walk; Canada Goose—eat water plants, swim.*]

Cud Chewers and Meat Eaters, pp. 163-166. The word "**herbivore**" means "plant-eater." The cow is an example of a herbivore and has a digestive system that is especially adapted to digest the fibers of grasses and plants. Its teeth are flat for grinding up grain and fibers, and there are millions of microorganisms in the first of the four stomach chambers that help break down the plant fibers. A "**carnivore**" is "meat-eater." The lion is an example of a carnivore. It has sharp teeth for tearing and biting meat. And its digestive system is shorter in proportion to the digestive system of herbivores. The word "**omnivore**" means "eater of both plants and animals." Most humans are omnivorous. Human intestines are long and complex, so they need fiber, such as grains and vegetables, to function well.

Let's see if you can figure out which of these animals are herbivores, which are carnivores, and which are omnivores. *(Write "herbivore", "carnivore", and "omnivore" on the blackboard.)*

As I read the list of animals to you, write them under the category to which they belong.

fox	deer	goat	kangaroo	zebra
rabbit	seal	lion	cat	giraffe
camel	horse	rat	eagle	vulture
sparrow	otter	raccoon	sheep	buffalo
elephant	bear	tiger	shark	parrot
crocodile	quail	rhinoceros	opossum	hyena

herbivore		carnivore		omnivore
rabbit	buffalo	fox	vulture	bear
camel	quail	seal	crocodile	opossum
rhinoceros	sparrow	cat	shark	rat
elephant	parrot	otter		raccoon
deer	giraffe	hyena		
horse	zebra	eagle		
goat	sheep	tiger		
kangaroo		lion		

Now, cut out the boxes from the *Cud Chewers and Meat Eaters (page 2)* and glue them in reverse order onto the *Cud Chewers and Meat Eaters* page. Then glue the column of Herbivore information face up onto the right side of the *Cud Chewers and Meat Eaters* page. Follow the directions for coloring each step of digestion. Then follow the directions beneath the lion for coloring the steps of digestion of carnivores.

Forest Food Chain, p. 167. Each animal has its own unique place in a food chain. Some animals eat plants while some eat other animals. Food is eaten to provide the energy necessary to continue life. An animal must eat either plants or other animals that have eaten plants. Plants, in turn, make their own food from energy they get from the sun. Thus, ultimately all energy comes from the sun (actually the capital "S"—Son of God; see John 1:1-3 and Heb. 1:1-3). Draw arrows to point toward what each animal eats.

[*Answers: plants*—>*sun; insect*—>*plants; toad*—>*insect; snake*—>*toad, insect; salamander*—> *insect, frog; skunk*—>*salamander, insect; squirrel*—>*plants; deer*—>*plants; rabbit*—>*plants; bird*—>*plants, insect; wild cat*—>*squirrel, bird; bear*—>*plants, deer, squirrel; fox*—>*squirrel, bird, insect, rabbit, snake, salamander; wolf*—>*skunk, squirrel, rabbit, deer*]

Prey for a Year, pp. 169-172. On the savannas of Africa, there is another food chain. Let's focus only on the lions for now and see how many animals it takes to feed a pride of five lions. Cut out *Prey for a Year (page 2)* and glue it onto the *Prey for a Year* page, so that it can fold out and you can see how many animals there are. Color the animals, and then count how many there are of each kind. Many groups of animals have been counted for you and have the total written on them. Add all these groups plus the individual animals and write in that number at the bottom of the page. *(You may want to do this as a class with younger students.)* [**Answers**: *Wildebeests, 107; Zebras, 33; Thompson's Gazelles, 25; Buffaloes, 12; Giraffes, 9; Hartebeests, 5; Impalas, 9; Elands, 5; other 14; total, 219. How many lions does this feed for a year? 5*]

Feeding the Multitudes, pp. 173-176. Although the lions (actually the lionesses) kill the animals, many other animals feed off the leftovers. Cut and glue (in reverse order) the pages from *Feeding the Multitudes (page 2)* on the *Feeding the Multitudes* page. At the bottom, color in the graph to show how many hours lions spend eating, walking, and resting in a day.

REVIEW: 1. How much water is in a fish? [*67%*]
2. What are two purposes of water for animals? [*helps distribute nutrients and oxygen; carries away wastes*]
3. What is the source of all energy? [*the sun (in the material world), God (in the spiritual)*]
4. How many different kinds of animals can eat from the meat of one wildebeest? [*lions, jackals, hyenas, carrion birds and insects*]
5. How can you tell where a particular type of bird lives and what it eats? [*by its beak and feet*] Give some examples. [*Toucans eat fruit and they perch on branches; eagles tear prey and grasp prey; also, see Beaks and Feet Show Where Birds Live and What They Eat*]
6. What are two differences between herbivores and carnivores? [*herbivores have flat teeth, a long digestive system and special microorganisms in the stomach; carnivores have sharp teeth and a shorter digestive system*]

Have the student explain his notebook page to a friend or relative and tell what he learned from the lesson. Also, review the songs/poems, and activities.

DIGGING DEEPER: 1. Explore the **ecosystem** of somewhere in your neighborhood such as a pond, field, or wooded area. Write a report or draw a picture of what you learned.

LESSON 24: Animal Reproduction/Genetics

PREPARATION: *Student will need* **notebook pp. 177-182**, *crayons, scissors, glue, and a pencil. You will need two coins, five prepared "eyes" (see the activity), and cellophane tape. You may want to divide this lesson into two parts.*

VOCABULARY:
        dominant: the predominant influence [L. *dominari,* to be master]
        fertile: able to reproduce [L. *fertilis,* fruitful]
        gene: the hereditary unit that passes hereditary characteristics from parent to child
            [Gk. *genos,* origin]
        genetics: the study of heredity [Gk. *gignesthai,* to be born]

heredity: passing on characteristics from parents to child [L. *heres*, an heir]
oviparous: hatched, born from an egg [L. *ovum*, an egg + *parere*, to give birth]
recessive: the receding or lesser influence [L. *recessus*, to recede]
reproduce: to multiply or produce living individuals
     [L. *re-*, again + *pro-*, forward + *ducere*, to lead]
sterile: barren, unable to reproduce [L. *sterilis*, barren]
viviparous: born alive [L. *vivus*, living + *parere*, to give birth]

INTRODUCTION: From the very beginning of creation, God designed each animal to be able to **reproduce** its own kind. He created male and female, and from these, more animals were born. Some animals are **viviparous** or born alive from their mothers. Others are **oviparous** or hatched from eggs. But each baby grows up to be like its adult parents. Part of how this happens is from the information that is put into the part of the cell called the **gene**. The study of genes is called **genetics**.

SONG/POEM:

> **Wouldn't This World be Crazy?**
> If a kangaroo could have a kitten,
> And a dog could have a calf,
> Wouldn't this world be crazy,
> Wouldn't your mother laugh?
> Because you might be a monkey
> And swing from tree to tree
> Or you might even be a fishy
> And swim in the deep blue sea.
>
> But God made each creature special
> Each one makes its own kind
> So you'll never see a doggy mooing
> And your mother won't lose her mind.
> Because she knows you are a human
> Though you might swing in a tree,
> And you'll never be a real live fishy
> Though you swim in the deep blue sea.

BIBLE READING: *(Have student look up Scriptures.)* **Heredity** plays a powerful part in how we look physically. We are told that Adam became the father of a son (Seth) who was like him (Genesis 5:3). We often notice similarities in people who are related. More importantly, we can see the results of our spiritual heritage. All people, as a result of sin, have the same relationship to God. They are separated from Him by sin through the sin of our common ancestor, the first Adam (Romans 5:12–14). But through Jesus (who is also called the last Adam) comes adoption into God's family (Romans 5:15–21; 1 Corinthians 15:45–50). And when we love Jesus, we reflect the characteristics of our adopted Father by practicing right living (Ephesians 5:1–6; 1 John 3:9), by loving one another (1 John 4:7, 5:1–3), and by overcoming evil in the world (1 John 5:4–5). What are some things you can do today to show people who your spiritual Father is?

NOTEBOOK: *Each After Its Own Kind, pp. 177-182.* God was very creative when it came to the ways that His creatures reproduced. Although there are similarities in the way many animals reproduce, each is also unique. The animals on this page are all mammals, but look at all the fascinating differences between them. Color and cut out the parts of *Each After Its Own Kind (page 2)* and glue them onto the *Each After Its Own Kind* page. We will go over the page and discuss it together when you are finished.

Egg Factory, pp. 183-186. Birds are **oviparous**, that is, they are nourished by the yolk within an egg and then hatched from that egg. Have you ever wondered how an egg was formed? The process is much like a conveyer belt in a factory. Color and cut out the parts on *Egg Factory (page 2)* and glue them on the *Egg Factory* page. Then color and cut out the developing chick and glue it inside its egg. Next, cut out the rest of the eggs and glue them into a little booklet on the bottom of the page. When you finish, let's read aloud the steps that go into making an egg.

The Kingdom of Living Things, pp. 187-190. In the 1700's a Swedish scientist by the name of Carolus Linnaeus was so intrigued by the order and design he observed in God's creation that he developed a system of classification that is still used today. Though evolutionists have tried to use the system to verify evolution, the classifications actually demonstrate that each living thing reproduces ONLY after its own kind. There is no natural interbreeding between animals in different classifications. *(See additional comment under EVOLUTION STUMPERS in this lesson.)*

Living things are divided by their common characteristics into five main groups (kingdoms). Two of the groups have members so small that they can only be seen with a microscope (monera and protist). The other three groups are the fungi, the plant, and the animal kingdom. Each of these kingdoms is broken down into smaller and smaller groups that have more specific characteristics in common. We will be working with the animal kingdom, which is divided into ten groups (phyla). These groups are further divided into "classes", then into "orders", then into "families", and finally into "genera", and "species." Each individual creature is given a family and a species name so that scientists around the world can identify any given animal exactly.

Let's see how this classification works. Glue *The Kingdom of Living Things (page 2)* onto the bottom of *The Kingdom of Living Things.* You will be using these charts to fill out the *Classifying Animals, pp. 191-192.*

Look at page 191. Let's do the first one together. The animal is a deer. Look at *The Kingdoms of Living Things* page and start at the top of the page. What kingdom does the deer belong to, plant or animal? [*the animal kingdom*] The next step is to decide which phylum; invertebrate (without backbones) or vertebrate (with backbones)? [*vertebrate*] Now, which class does the deer belong to; fish, amphibian, reptile, bird, or mammal? [*mammal*] Now look on the chart for a picture of an animal that looks like a deer. Which order does it belong to? [*artiodactyla*] What are some of the distinctive features of that order? [*even-toed hooves, eat plants*] Next, which family does the deer belong to? [*4. cervidae*] Look at the chart again. What are some other species that belong to the same family? [*elk, reindeer*] Mark each answer on your page and then use the same procedure to classify the rest of the animals on the two *Classifying Animals* pages.

[Answers: p. 191, 192]

animal (species)	kingdom	phylum	class	order	sub-order	family
deer	animal	vertebrate	mammal	artiodactyla		cervidae
right whale	animal	vertebrate	mammal	cetacea	mysticeti	
zebra	animal	vertebrate	mammal	perissodactyla		equidae
camel	animal	vertebrate	mammal	artiodactyla		camelidae
armadillo	animal	vertebrate	mammal	endentata		
giant panda	animal	vertebrate	mammal	carnivora		ailuro-podidae
giraffe	animal	vertebrate	mammal	artiodactyla		giraffidae
flying fox	animal	vertebrate	mammal	chiroptera	mega-chiroptere	
wolf	animal	vertebrate	mammal	carnivora		canidae

page 192	kingdom	phylum	class	order	sub-order	family
bear	animal	vertebrate	mammal	carnivora		ursidae
elephant	animal	vertebrate	mammal	proboscidea		
rhinoceros	animal	vertebrate	mammal	perissodactyla		rhinocerotidae
mouse	animal	vertebrate	mammal	rodentia	myomorpha	
raccoon	animal	vertebrate	mammal	carnivora		procyonidae
rabbit	animal	vertebrate	mammal	lagomorpha		
bison	animal	vertebrate	mammal	artiodactyla		bovidae
kangaroo	animal	vertebrate	mammal	marsupialia		
lion	animal	vertebrate	mammal	carnivora		felidae

ACTIVITY: *(This would be a good stopping point if you are dividing the lesson.)* Let's play a game together before we do the next notebook pages. It is called the **Gene Pool Game** and will help us to figure out what genes will be available for the eye color of several children.

blue	**blue**	**blue**	**Brown**	**Brown**

  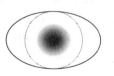  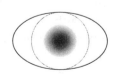

Gene Pool Game: You will need two quarters. Trace and cut out the five "eyes" above. Color three of the "eyes" blue, and two of the "eyes" brown. Tape a brown "eye" on each side of one coin, which will represent the father's genes. Tape a blue "eye" on each side of the other coin, which will represent the mother's genes. Their children would receive one eye color gene from each parent. To show how this works, we will flip both coins to see what genes each child will get. It is important to know that the brown eye gene is dominant. That means it dominates, or wins out over, the blue eye gene. If even one brown eye gene shows up, the child will have brown eyes. Toss both coins five times. Each time the coins are flipped, we will see what eye color genes another child of theirs would inherit. What was the outcome? [*All the children will have one brown gene from the father, and one blue gene from the mother. Brown is dominant so all the children will have brown eyes.*]

Now, take one brown eye gene from the father, and trade places with the blue eye gene from the mother. Both the mother and father have a "dominant" brown eye gene and a "recessive" blue eye gene. This means that both parents have brown eyes but that some of the children may get blue eyes. Toss the coins five more times and keep track of your results. If two blue genes show up, the child will have blue eyes. If even one brown eye gene shows up, the child will have brown eyes. What are the results? [*Results will vary, but there could be a child with blue eyes*]

Let's do it again with one more combination. This time the father will have one brown eye gene and one blue eye gene, and the mother will have two blue eye genes. Toss the coins five more times and keep track of your results. If two blue genes show up, the child will have blue eyes. If even one brown eye gene shows up, the child will have brown eyes. What are the results? [*Results will vary, but there will be a greater chance for blue eyes*]

NOTEBOOK: *Guess Genes for Guinea Pigs, p. 193.* The **genes** are the part of the cell that contains the information of all the characteristics of the parent. In the process of reproduction, genes from the father combine with genes from the mother and new possibilities are created. There are two genes for the color of the guinea pig's fur. We will start out with a brown guinea pig with both fur-color genes the same, and a white guinea pig with both fur-color genes the same. The white color is **recessive** and the brown is **dominant**. This means that if just one part is brown, the color of the guinea pig will be brown, even if one part is white. Now let's work with this project on your notebook *Guess Genes for Guinea Pigs* page. The different types of lines show you which gene the offspring gets from each parent. Write in the capital 'B' when the gene will be brown, and the lower case 'b' for the white gene. Then color the guinea pigs the color that they will be. Remember, brown is dominant and wins over white!
[***Answers:*** *Row 1—Bb, Bb, Bb, Bb. (all colored brown) Row 2—BB, Bb, bB, bb. (first three colored brown, last, white) Row 3—Bb, Bb, bb, bb. (first two brown, last two white)*]

Breeding Domestic Chickens, p. 194. (Help younger students with this page.) The study of **genetics** is very complex. There are so many characteristics and possible combinations for each thing! For example, consider your extended family members. They all have some of the same ancestors, and yet they each look different. The chickens that we will be studying today have the same grandparents and parents, but what will all the chicks be like? Figure out the combination of the genes, and then look at the picture at the top to draw in the combs of the offspring. You will get two genes from the mother (directly above), and two genes from the father (to the left). Put the r's together and the a's together. If there is a capital letter, put it first. Now look at the chickens above and figure out which comb and wattle (the growth under the chicken's chin) the offspring would have. Then draw it in. When you are finished, write in at the top how many out of the sixteen have walnut combs, how many have rose combs, how many have pea combs, and how many have single combs. Let's do the first one together. This chick will get a capital 'R' from both its father and mother, so put two capital R's together in the box. It also gets a capital 'A' from its father and its mother. Put the two capital A's after the r's. We now have 'RRAA'. Next look above and see what that combination will be. [*walnut*]

[**Answers:** *walnut: 9/16   rose: 3/16   pea: 3/16   single: 1/16*]

RRAA	RRAa	RrAA	RrAa
RRAa	RRaa	RrAa	Rraa
RrAA	RrAa	rrAA	rrAa
RrAa	Rraa	rrAa	rraa

EVOLUTION STUMPERS: When a donkey and a horse (two closely related animals) mate, a mule is produced. However, the mule is unable to have offspring. (It is **sterile**.) If even closely related animals can't have **fertile** offspring, how did a male and female of each species manage to evolve to the same stage at the same time, to find each other, and to create a whole new species?

REVIEW: 1. What is genetics? [*the study of heredity*]
2. Why isn't it possible for dogs to have kittens? [*God created creatures to reproduce after their own kind*]

TEST: *Student will need **notebook p. 252,** Crossword Review 8. Use as a review or test for older students.* **Answers:** *Teacher's p. 126.*

Have the student explain his notebook page to a friend or relative.

DIGGING DEEPER: 1. Fill out a *Scientist Detective* page for Gregor Mendel (1822–1884), Walter S. Sutton (1877–1916), or Thomas Hunt Morgan (1866–1945), pioneers in the field of genetics. 2. Fill out a *Scientist Detective* page for Carolus Linnaeus (1707–1778), the Swedish scientist who developed the system for classification of living things. 3. Do a report on hybrid grains and animals. (County extension offices often have free information available.) 4. Fill out a *Scientist Detective* page for Charles Darwin (1809–1882), the "father" of evolution. 5. Study *Creation Anatomy: A Study Guide to the Miracles of the Body!* by Felice Gerwitz & Jill Whitlock, Media Angels, 15720 S. Pebble Lane, Fort Myers, FL, 33912-2341. 6. Read Chapter 1, "Likeness" from *In His Image*, by Dr. Paul Brand & Phillip Yancy, Zondervan Publishing House, Grand Rapids, MI, 1984.

LESSON 25: Animal Instinct, Vision and Brains

PREPARATION: *Student will need **notebook pp. 195-203**, crayons, scissors, a pencil, and glue. Vocabulary words may be written on flash cards.*

VOCABULARY:
      cerebellum: the smaller, back portion of brain; controls voluntary muscles and balance
          [L. *cerebrum*, the brain]
      cerebrum: largest part of brain, center of intelligence, movement [L. *cerebrum*, the brain]
      instinct: inborn ability to do certain actions without being taught
      medulla: lowest portion of brain; controls involuntary breathing and heartbeat
          [L. *medulla*, marrow]

migration: to go from one place to another (in search of warmer climates for breeding and food) [L. *migrare*, to go]

olfactory bulb: center for smell [L. *olere*, to smell + *facere*, to make]

optic lobes: center for sight [Gk. *optikos*, vision]

pecten: pleats of tissue that carry extra blood (as to eye of hawk)

pituitary gland: gland which controls growth and other functions

tapetum: membrane in cat's eye that reflects light like a mirror [L. *pituita*, mucus]

INTRODUCTION: Each animal that God created fits into its own special niche. Its limbs are just right for how it moves, its mouth is just right for what it eats, in fact, everything about it is just right. Each animal also has a particular function in the scope of creation. Some are grazers and depend only on plants for their food. Others are hunters and they help to prevent overpopulation of animals that reproduce rapidly (like rabbits). Still others are the clean-up crews. These scavengers clean up the leftovers so that nothing is wasted or left to cause disease. How are each of these animals able to obtain food and shelter, and to care for their young so that their species will continue? Through what we call instinct, God has instilled the necessary knowledge and abilities into each creature that allow them to survive and care for their young.

BIBLE READING: *(Have student look up Scriptures.)* We can know a lot about instinct in different animals, but it is humbling to realize that we have no control over it. Job realized God's power over nature in Job 39 and 42:1-6. Let's read those verses together.

NOTEBOOK: *Migration, pp. 195-198. (With younger students, you may want to do this page together as a class.)* Instinct is one of God's amazing provisions for His creation. One of the most interesting instincts is the unerring patterns of migration that many animals follow, allowing them to travel from cold areas, that do not have much food, to warm areas during the winter. One tiny bundle of courage is the Arctic tern which flies from the North Pole to the South Pole, and benefits from the abundance of summer food in both places. Cut out and glue the "Migration Routes" from *Migration (page 2)* on the right side of the *Migration* page. Then cut out each of the animals on the dotted lines. Figure out each migration path from the clues and glue the animal onto the correct circle. When you are finished, we will go over it together. *(Read the clues aloud for younger students.)*

The Eyes Have It, pp. 199-202. The eyes of each animal are just exactly right for its particular needs. The hawk, for example, must be able to see small objects from great distances so that it can focus on a tiny mouse from high in the sky. Grazing animals need to be able to focus on what they are eating as well as to watch for any danger that might be nearby. And insects pick up light waves that humans are unable to see so that they can find the right kind of flowers. Cut out the boxes on *The Eyes Have It (page 2)* and glue them to their corresponding letter on *The Eyes Have It* page. You will be making little booklets. The left side will have only one lift-up page, the right side will have two lift-up pages. When you are finished, we will go over it together.

Brains, p. 203. Each animal's brain is very complex, capable, and designed to meet the needs of that animal. Many animals have very accurate senses of smell, hearing, physical coordination, and touch. For each of the animals on the *Brains* page, locate and color the part of the brain according to the corresponding color code. Notice the brains of the larger animals are much bigger than those of the smaller animals. These larger brains have areas that control smell, sight, and movement as well. The animals with larger brains are more intelligent and trainable than animals with smaller, less complex brains. When you finish, we will go over the page together.

REVIEW: 1. Why do animals migrate? [*to search for warmer climates for food and breeding*]
2. How are the eyes of a hawk different from the eyes of a cat? [*a hawk's eyes have pecten so they can see small objects from great distances; a cat's eyes have tapetum so they can see very well in the dark*]
3. What is unique about the eyes of grazing animals? [*they can focus on what they are eating while watching for predators at the same time*]
4. Which sense is interpreted by the olfactory bulb? [*smell*]

Have the student explain his notebook page to a friend or relative and tell what he learned from the lesson.

DIGGING DEEPER: 1. Write a report about how migration patterns of birds have been tracked. 2. Find out more about animal instinct and give a report to the class. 3. Research and draw a picture of several animals that hibernate. You might draw a snow scene and have a lift-up window over the place where each animal is hibernating.

LESSON 26: Animal Ecology

Animal ecology will be presented in two lessons.

LESSON 26:A Extinction

PREPARATION: *Student will need* **notebook pp. 204-207,** *crayons, scissors, a pencil, and glue. Vocabulary words may be written on flash cards.*

VOCABULARY:
> **baleen**: a sieve-like bone structure in the mouth of one group of whales that allows the whale to strain out the tiny shrimp, plankton, and krill from the ocean water [L. *balaena*, a whale]
> **endangered**: threatened with extinction [*en-*, in, with + M.E. *danger*, power]
> **extinct**: no living specimens or survivors [L.*extinctus*, dead, extinguished]
> **toothed (odontoid)**: the second group of whales which have teeth, and eat fish and other sea creatures.

INTRODUCTION: When the natural ecosystem or balance of nature is disturbed, sometimes whole groups of animals die out. When there are no more animals of a particular species, that type of animal is said to be **extinct**. This often happens when humans hunt and kill more animals than are necessary, such as what happened with the beautiful carrier pigeon, and almost happened to bison and some whales.

BIBLE READING: *(Have student look up Scriptures.)* From the beginning of creation, man was given the responsibility to care for creation (Genesis 1:31, Psalm 8:6-8). God is so aware of each of His creatures that He knows when even a tiny sparrow falls to the ground (Matthew 10: 29). What are some of the things that you can do to help care for God's creation?

NOTEBOOK: *Extinct is Forever, pp. 204-206.* Cut out the pictures from the lower part of the *Extinct is Forever (page 2).* When you have them all ready, we will do the page together. Then make these pages into a booklet by gluing or stapling them in reverse order on the *Extinct is Forever* page. I will read the story of the passenger pigeon to you. As I read it, I will give instruction on how and where to glue the pictures on the pages.

The passenger pigeon was a beautiful gray bird with a slate blue head and wine-colored breast. (glue on the bird) In the early 1800's, historians recorded seeing so many of the passenger pigeons that the sun was actually blacked out for hours as these birds flew by. (glue birds over the sun) Passenger pigeons were the most common bird in the Americas. About four out of every ten birds were passenger pigeons. (glue on the four small pigeons) There were even more passenger pigeons than there are people on earth today! (9 billion). (glue on the earth) There were so many birds, that when they roosted in the trees, their droppings would collect to up to six inches deep. (glue the birds on the branch) As America developed, farmers began cutting down the trees needed by the pigeons for food and shelter. (glue on farmers cutting down the trees) Since the passenger pigeons only laid one egg at a time, when storms killed millions, they could not reproduce rapidly. In addition, hunters began to shoot the birds. They could sell each one for only a penny. Even so, some hunters killed so many that they made $1,000 a week. To do that, they were killing one hundred thousand birds every week. (glue on the killed birds) Thousands were killed by toxic smoke and by shooting them, while many were captured in nets. (glue on these items) During this time, there would be up to three train cars full of pigeons that had been captured for their meat, feather pillows, and for shooting matches. By 1900 only one passenger pigeon was left. (glue on the last pigeon) Her name was Martha. A reward of $1,000 was offered to anyone who could find a mate for her. None was found. Martha died on September 1, 1914, and the passenger pigeon passed into extinction. Within the space of a person's lifetime, this once innumerable bird was gone forever. There are no more passenger pigeons for you to glue on.

The bison (buffalo) was another animal that was widely hunted. It became extinct in the wild. If it were not for wildlife refuges and ranchers raising them, bison might have become extinct altogether. Read about the bison and color the areas directed on the map of the USA on the *Extinct is Forever* page.

REVIEW: 1. What are some of the factors that make a group of animals extinct? [*a disruption of their ecosystem; hunters killing more animals than can be replaced*]
2. How many passenger pigeons were there in the early 1800's? [*9 billion*]
3. Why were the pigeons hunted? [*for meat, feather pillows, and shooting matches*]
4. Why were bison hunted? [*for meat, hides, sport*]

DIGGING DEEPER: 1. Find out what animals are threatened by extinction today. What is being done to protect them? How does this protection affect humans? How can a balance be achieved in this area? When there is a conflict, is it more important to protect endangered animals or humans? 2. Visit a wildlife refuge in your area.

LESSON 26 B: Whales

INTRODUCTION: Whales are ocean-living mammals, and are among the largest creatures on our planet. They give birth to live young, and nourish them with milk. They must surface for air, since they breathe with lungs. The two large families of whales are the **toothed** whales and the **baleen** whales. Toothed whales have teeth, and eat fish and squid. The brains of the toothed whales are proportionately quite large for their bodies. Baleen whales have baleen plates in their mouths that serve to strain the water for their food which includes plankton and krill, tiny sea plants and creatures. Isn't it incredible that the largest creatures on earth eat some of the smallest food on earth? Did you ever think that whales would have earrings? They do, but not like ours! The age of baleen whales can be estimated by the yearly rings in their ears that are similar to the rings in tree trunks.

NOTEBOOK: *A Whale of Information, p. 207. (For younger students, write the underlined answers on the blackboard. Note: Almost all the **numbers are very approximate** due to the difficulty involved in trying to count whales.)* Let's go on a whaling adventure and learn more about eight different kinds of whales. First, color each of the whales the colors indicated on each one. Then I will be reading information about the whales to you and will give you time to fill in each answer on your page. For each whale, we will talk about how many whales there were before commercial whaling and how many there are now. You are to color in the graphs up to the number of whales that there were then in the first column, and the number there are now in the second column. In the late 1800's, whales were hunted and killed for their oil and other products. Because of the unlimited killing, many groups of whales were close to extinction. Laws were developed to protect these whales. Mark whether the whale is an endangered species. Also mark if it is baleen or toothed. Listen carefully and write in the length and weight. And finally, write in the interesting facts that make each whale unique.

The Humpback
The <u>humpback</u> whale has a flat head, long flippers, and a hump on its back. It is black with white areas on the belly. It is a <u>baleen</u> whale *(pause)* that weighs from <u>40–50 tons</u> *(pause)* and grows to <u>45 feet</u> in length. *(pause)* Because the humpback moves slowly and is rich in oil, it was hunted and killed. It has been under protection since <u>1966</u>. *(pause)* It is no longer listed as an endangered species but is still <u>vulnerable</u> to extinction. This protection makes it against the law to hunt them. Before commercial whaling began, there were <u>150,000</u>. *(pause)* Today the population is up from 7,000 to about <u>20,000</u>. *(pause)* The humpback is playful and does somersaults. The males in each region have beautiful and distinctive songs that they sing for up to 22 hours at a time. *(pause)*

The Fin
The <u>fin</u> whale is the second largest whale. A newborn fin whale is around 20 feet long and weighs 2 tons. The adults may weigh <u>50-70 tons</u> *(pause)* and be up to <u>80 feet</u> long. *(pause)* They are <u>baleen</u> whales and can live 70–80 years. *(pause)* In the early 1900's, there were an estimated <u>one million</u> (<u>1,000,000</u>) fin whales. *(pause)* Now there are approximately <u>60,000</u>. *(pause)* It is no longer listed as an endangered species but is still <u>vulnerable</u> to extinction. *(pause)*

The Orca

The orca is the official name for the killer whale. It is a toothed *(pause)* whale that is found in every ocean of the world. Orcas live in pods or families of 3–30 whales and hunt for food (mostly fish and seals) in a pack. *(pause)* They have been friendly and gentle to humans and are related to the dolphins. *(pause)* The orca whales may reach up to 30 feet in length *(pause)* and weigh from 6–8 tons. *(pause)* They have not been popular for commercial whaling and are not listed as endangered or protected by law. *(pause)*

The Blue

The blue whale is the largest creature on earth. *(pause)* It averages 75-80 feet in length *(pause)* and weigh from 106–150 tons. *(pause)* Its name comes from the light blue color of its skin. The blue whales may travel in a family group or alone as they migrate from the Antarctic in the summer to the tropics in the winter. They are baleen whales. *(pause)* The blue whales were listed as a protected and endangered species in 1966 *(pause)* because their numbers have decreased to less than 1% of their former population—from 1,300,000 *(pause)* to only 10,000 today. *(pause)*

The Right

The right whale was called the right whale because it was considered the "right" whale to hunt. These whales were popular to kill because they were easy to spot with their distinctive double spouts, they were slow swimmers and were playful and tame. They also floated when they were killed. The right whale became protected in 1935 *(pause)* because their numbers had been 50,000 before commercial whaling began. *(pause)* Today they are quite rare and there are only about 1,000 of these endangered species left. *(pause)* The right whales are baleen whales *(pause)* that grow up to 50 feet in length *(pause)* and weigh from 82–106 tons. *(pause)* They have no dorsal fin but have a "bonnet" type growth on the front of the head. *(pause)*

The Bowhead

The bowhead whale is another one of the toothed whales. *(pause)* It lives only in the western Arctic waters. *(pause)* It grows to 60 feet in length *(pause)* and can weigh more than 60 tons. *(pause)* Because it swims slowly and is rich in oil, it has also been hunted to near extinction. It has been the primary source of food for Eskimos for hundreds of years and the attempts to protect it from extinction have presented great problems for the Eskimos. *(pause)* It became a protected species in 1946. *(pause)* The numbers were reduced from 50,000 *(pause)* to only about 10,000. *(pause)* The current population is only about 8,000 and it is listed as an endangered species.

The Sperm

The sperm whale is the largest toothed whale. *(pause)* Its favorite food is squid which it searches out by sending sonar-type clicks from the surface. When it discovers a squid it can dive straight down 3,000 feet and can stay under water for as long as 90 minutes. *(pause)* It may reach a length of up to 60 feet *(pause)* and weigh from 35-45 tons. *(pause)* The sperm whale numbered around 1,100,000 *(pause)* but were decreased by hunters to 500,000. Today they number more than 1,500,000. *(pause)* They are not protected by law. *(pause)* A sperm whale was made popular by the story of *Moby Dick*. *(pause)*

The Gray

The gray whale travels the farthest of any mammal. It covers about 16,000 miles in the round trip migration from the Arctic regions to Baja California where it breeds and calves in the warm lagoons. *(pause)*   The gray whale was protected in 1947 *(pause)* when it was so near extinction that there were only 250 left. *(pause)* As a result of this protection, there are about 22,000 gray whales today. *(pause)* It is no longer listed as an endangered species but is still vulnerable to extinction. *(pause)* It is a baleen whale *(pause)* and grows up to 50 feet in length. *(pause)*   It can weigh from 30-40 tons. *(pause)*

Whales

Name	Number then/**now**	Protected	Family	Endangered	Length in feet	Weight in tons	Facts (answers may vary)
Humpback	150,000 **20,000**	1966	Baleen	No (Vulnerable)	45	40–50	Males sing
Fin	1 million **60,000**		Baleen	No (Vulnerable)	80	50-70	Lives 70–80 yrs., 18–20' and 2 tons at birth
Orca (killer whale)	Unknown (thousands)		Toothed	No	30	6–8	Lives in families or pods (3–30)
Blue	1,300,000 **10,000**	1966	Baleen	Yes	75-80	106–150	Largest creature on planet
Right (Northern)	50,000 **1,000**	1935	Baleen	Yes	50	82–106	No dorsal fins; was "right" whale to hunt
Bowhead (near Alaska)	50,000 **8,000**	1946	Toothed	Yes	60	60	Eskimos hunt; lives in Arctic
Sperm	1,100,000 **1,500,000**		Toothed	No	60	35-45	Whale of *Moby Dick;* can dive 3,000' and stay down 90 min.
Gray	250 **22,000**	1947	Baleen	No (Vulnerable)	50	30-40	Longest migration of 16,000 miles

REVIEW: 1. Name the two major groups of whales. [*baleen, toothed*]
2. Which is the largest whale? [*Blue whale*]
3. Which whale has the longest migration? [*Gray whale*]
4. Which whale is the rarest? [*Right whale*]
5. Why is a whale classified as a mammal? [*gives birth to live young; provides milk for young;*
    breathes with lungs]

TEST: *Student will need **a copy student of p. 253**, Crossword Review 9. Use as a review or test for older student.* **Answers:** *Teacher's p. 127.*

Have the student explain his notebook page to a friend or relative.

DIGGING DEEPER: 1. Read books about whales or whaling such as *Moby Dick*. 2. Visit a large sea aquarium and actually see whales. 3. Research what has been done to try to protect whales. 4. Play a game called "Krill—A Whale of a Game" from Ampersand Press, 750 Lake St., Port Townsend, WA, 98368. 5. Compare the uses for the buffalo by the American Plains Indians before the 1800's and the uses for the whale by the Alaskan Natives today. 6. Do a research paper from newspapers, Internet or magazines for articles about current whale events. 7. Go to the *Creation Magazine* archives, at www.answersingenesis.org for the article entitled, "Whale Explodes Fossil Theory" by Tas Walker. Write a report on the conclusions. 8. Keep updated on current whale information at www.acsonline.org/factpack.

MAN: MADE IN GOD'S IMAGE

LESSON 27: Man—Reproductive System

PREPARATION: *Student will need* **notebook pp. 208-210**, *crayons, scissors, glue and pencil. You will also need the ingredients for making cookies for the activity. Vocabulary words may be written on flash cards.*

VOCABULARY:

> **ovum**: the female reproductive cell [L. *ovum*, an egg]
> **pregnant**: to be with child [L. *praegnans*, to be with child]
> **sperm**: the male reproductive cell [Gk. *sperma*, seed]
> **spirit**: the eternal part of man [L. *spirare*, to breathe]
> **uterus**: the womb; the female organ where a baby develops before birth
> > [L. *uterus*, womb]

INTRODUCTION: In many ways, both physically and biologically, humans fit into the category of mammals—they are warm-blooded with a four-chambered heart, they breathe oxygen with lungs, and they have hair. The females give birth to live young and produce milk to nurse their babies. But there is something that makes humans uniquely different from every other creature that God created—man was created in the image of God and has a soul and spirit. Physically, there are some very special things about humans, including the capacity of the human brain to create things of beauty; to develop both written and oral language; to pass information and history to future generations; to make inventions and discoveries; and to drastically change their environment (for the better or the worse). But the thing that really separates man from animals is our eternal **spirit**. Out of all creation, man, and man alone, has the ability to have a personal, loving relationship with God. The very God who created the whole universe carefully knit us together in our mother's womb. He never stops thinking about us or caring for us no matter where in the universe we are. So, as we study about our bodies, we can marvel over the way God carefully and wonderfully made our body.

SONG/POEM:

> **Psalm 139** (For Sheri, Wendy, and Christopher)
> You saw me when I was formed
> In the womb all alone.
> You knit me together there
> Your workmanship shows so much care.
>
> You recorded in Your Book
> Before a breath I ever took,
> Every minute of each day
> And every word that I would say.

And how precious it is, Lord,
And with joy my heart has soared,
For I can't count the times each day
That Your thoughts have turned my way.

If I go to a distant star
Or beneath the ground so far,
I could still hear Your call
For it was You who made it all.

The morning winds I could ride
To the world's other side.
For even there Your hand will guide,
In Your arms I'd still abide.

Even in the darkest night
I cannot hide from Your sight
Because darkness is as light
For Your love is shining bright.

In the past, as You have lead,
You laid Your hand upon my head.
Chart my path, for You know best
Where to walk and when to rest.

Test every thought I ever had.
Point out what has made You sad.
Cleanse my heart and make me true
And lead me home to be with You.

And how precious it is, Lord,
And with joy my heart has soared,
For I can't count the times each day
That Your thoughts have turned my way.

ACTIVITY: (*Bake chocolate chip, or oatmeal-raisin cookies and get out only one ingredient at a time. Do not tell the student what you are going to make and have him just add each thing as you give it to him. Talk about how this is like our life. We don't know what God is making out of our lives. And just like with the recipe, if we try to add something at the wrong time or add too much of one thing, we will not have God's best for our lives. Ecclesiastes 11:8–10, 12:1.*)

This would be an excellent opportunity to present the plan of salvation.
1. God loves you (John 3:16) 2. Your sins have separated you from God (Romans 3:23; 6:23) 3. God paid the price for your sins (1 Corinthians 15:3; Ephesians 2:8,9) 4. Receive and believe in Jesus Christ as your Savior (John 1:12; Acts 16:31). 5. Grow up in Jesus Christ (Colossians 2:6,7). This is a sample prayer you might use:

Dear God,

Thank you that you love me and that Jesus died to pay for my sins. I ask you to forgive me and to take charge of my life. I believe that Jesus is my Savior and I want to grow to be more like Him every day. Help me to tell everyone about you.

In Jesus Name,   AMEN

BIBLE READING: *(Have student look up Scriptures.)*   God made you to be uniquely you. He knew all about you even before you were born and He knit you together in your mother's womb (Ecclesiastes 11:5; Psalm 139). It is only by God's blessing that you can be alive (Acts 17:22–31). Every age and stage of our life has different responsibilities and capabilities. Babies are not able to do the things that children can do. And older people may not be able to do everything that young people can do. It is up to us to be what God wants us to be at each stage of our physical and spiritual development (1 Timothy 5:1–2; Titus 2:1–6; 1 John 2:1, 13, 14). Knowing God is the common denominator that helps us to interact with people of all ages.

SONG/POEM:

> **A Man of God** (Adam's Song)
> I don't care if you play football or play in the band,
> I don't care if you're a doctor or a garbage man,
> It doesn't matter if you're good in school or great at art,
> There's just one thing I care with all my heart;
>
> That you grow up to be a man of God,
> That you use His Word as a measuring rod,
> That you love your neighbor as yourself,
> That you do not trust in this world's wealth,
> That you grow up to be a man of God.
>
> I don't care if you're a loner or have lots of friends,
> I don't care if your clothes are new or they have lots of mends,
> It doesn't matter if you're tall and thin, or short and round,
> There's just one important thing that I have found;
>
> That you grow up to be a man of God,
> That you use His Word as a measuring rod,
> That you love your neighbor as yourself,
> That you do not trust in this world's wealth,
> That you grow up to be a man of God.

NOTEBOOK: *Wonderfully Made, pp. 208-210.* The **reproductive system** is one of the body's ten major systems. Its purpose is to produce the reproductive cells and is different in men and women. God planned this for us to be able to have children. He planned for one man and one woman who love God and each other, to marry so they could make a safe and happy place for their children to be born and grow up. It is totally awesome to consider how a baby is formed! At conception, two tiny cells, one from the mother (the **ovum**) and one from the father (the **sperm**), come together, and after nine months of growing in the womb (**uterus**), a wonderful little baby is ready to be born. *(This might be a good time to continue "sex education" as appropriate for your students.)* Cut out the pictures of the baby on *Wonderfully Made (p. 2)* and glue them in place. You can see from this picture that when a woman is **pregnant**, there is a real live baby in her! Then cut out the pictures of the boy and glue them **face down** and in reverse order, so that you can watch the boy grow up as you turn the pages.

REVIEW: 1. What do humans have that animals do not? [*an eternal spirit*]
2. What is God's plan for having babies? [*for one man and one woman who love God and each other, to marry so they could make a safe and happy place for their children to be born and grow up*]

Have the student explain his notebook page to a friend or relative and tell what he learned from the lesson.

DIGGING DEEPER: 1. Begin reading *Fearfully and Wonderfully Made*, by Dr. Paul Brand & Phillip Yancy, Zondervan Publishing House, Grand Rapids, MI, 1980. 2. Summarize, in an outline form, the preparation and requirements needed to become an M.D. (doctor of medicine) or D.O. (doctor of osteopathy). 3. Take a first aid class from your local Red Cross Chapter. 4. What is the biblical view of abortion? If one set of parents believed that man "evolved" and is "disposable" and another set of parents believed that God created man with an eternal soul, knit him together in his mother's womb, and scheduled every day of his life before his first breath, how would these views affect the way each regarded their unborn child? Discuss some of these differences. 5. Read Chapter 17, "Listening", from *In His Image*, by Dr. Paul Brand & Phillip Yancy, Zondervan Publishing House, Grand Rapids, MI, 1984. 6. Watch the video, *Human Life*, from Moody Institute of Science, 820 N. La Salle Blvd, Chicago, IL, 60610, 1995.

LESSON 28: The Cell

PREPARATION: *Student will need **notebook pp. 211-216**, crayons, scissors, glue and a pencil. Vocabulary words may be written on flash cards.*

VOCABULARY:

> **cell membrane:** the covering of the cell, which acts like a "guarded wall", controlling what enters or leaves the cell [L. *membrana*, parchment]
> **cell:** the simplest unit of structure of living things [L. *cella*, a small room]
> **centrioles:** rod-shaped structures that function like "magnets" during cell division
> **chromosomes:** contain the cell's genetic information [Gk. *chroma*, color + *soma*, a body]
> **DNA:** (deoxyribonucleic acid) an arrangement of nucleic acids that contain the genetic "master plan"
> **endoplasmic reticulum:** sheets of membrane that provide "transportation" for protein within the cell
> **Golgi body:** a group of flattened membrane sacs that "package" protein
> **lysosomes:** the "garbage disposal system" of the cell, which dispose of invading materials and bacteria
> **mitochondria:** are the cell's "power plants" and produce the cell's energy

nucleus: the "control center" of the cell which controls and directs all the cell's activities [L. *nucleus*, kernel]

INTRODUCTION: Our bodies are made up of about 100 trillion cells. Each **cell** is an amazing self-contained unit, and yet they all work together to make up "you." We each began with one cell. Within that one cell was all the information to make you—your eye and hair color; how tall you would grow; if you will become bald; if you would enjoy music or math. Yes, some of that is affected by your environment and diet, but a lot of it was "written" within that cell. That simple cell began to divide and multiply. From that one cell came cells that became your heart, other cells, your feet and so on. All your cells followed the "master plan" found in that first cell.

BIBLE READING: *(Have student look up Scriptures.)* Can you imagine what you would be like if your body just had muscles? What if it just had bones? How about if you were just one big eye? Or if you were only a foot? Each part of your body plays an important part for the whole and they all work together as a whole. Each cell of your body contains the recipe (DNA) for your whole body and yet each cell performs specific functions. The purpose of all of creation was not just for God to reveal Himself to man, but that man might respond to His love. And that all men (and women, boys and girls), in spite of being more diverse than the millions of cells in your body, might function as one body, His CHURCH (Ephesians 3:8–19, 4:4–16). Jesus' last prayer with His disciples before He was crucified was for us. He prayed that we would be one so the world would believe the Father had sent Him (John 17:15–26). An early church father had this helpful advice for practicing unity: "In essentials, unity; in non-essentials, liberty; in all things, charity [love]." What can we do to fulfill Jesus' prayer for unity in His church?

NOTEBOOK: *Cell City, pp. 211-216.* Each cell works like an efficiently run city, with all the parts cooperating. Let's do a page about the cell. Cut and glue the *Cell City (page 2)* onto the *Cell City* page. Look at the pictures in each box. With a straight edge, draw a line to the corresponding part in the cell. Now read the clues and figure out the functions of each part of the cell. Cut and glue the pictures from *Cell City (page 3)* to the function they represent on the *Cell City* page. When you are done, we will go over the page together.

TEST: *Student will need* **notebook p. 254,** *Crossword Review 10. Use as a review or test for older students.* **Answers:** *Teacher's p. 127.*

DIGGING DEEPER: 1. Research genetic engineering in plants and animals. Formulate your position on cloning. Is it OK for animals (such as the sheep, "Dolly")? Is it OK for humans? 2. Study genetic testing as used for determining ancestry (whether or not someone is a descendant of a particular person). 3. Study *Creation Anatomy: A Study Guide to the Miracles of the Body!* by Felice Gerwitz & Jill Whitlock, Media Angels, 15720 S. Pebble Lane, Fort Myers, FL, 33912-2341.

LESSON 29: Man—Skeletal System

PREPARATION: *Student will need **notebook pp. 217-226**, crayons, scissors, glue and a pencil. You will need "splints" (such as a magazine, piece of cardboard or folded towel), "slings" (such as a dish towel or baby blanket), and ice in a zipped plastic bag for the activity.*

VOCABULARY:
> **ligaments:** strong fibers that connect the bones [L. *ligare*, to bind]
> **marrow:** the soft center of bones [O.E. *meary*, marrow]
> **skeleton:** the framework of the body [Gk. *skeletos*, dried up]

INTRODUCTION: Skeletal System. The skeletal system is the frame for our body. Our 206 bones hold us up and make it possible for us to move. Bones also protect our important inner parts. The cranium (skull) is like a helmet that protects our brain. The ribs form a cage that protects our heart and lungs. The backbone (spinal column) is fantastically arranged to allow movement as well as to protect the spinal cord. The smallest bones are inside our ears, enabling us to hear. The largest and longest bones are in our legs, enabling us to walk and supporting the weight of our body. The long bones produce new red blood cells that are formed in the **marrow** or middle of the long bones. The bones are joined by rubber–like **ligaments**. Babies have more bones than adults and their bones are very soft. As we grow, some of these bones fuse or grow together and become harder. Bones are alive. If we break a bone, it will grow back together if we keep the broken parts close together. That is why we use stiff casts for broken bones. We will be learning more about these wonderful bones of ours in this lesson.

SONG/POEM:
> **The Skeletal System**
> The bones are where we start with the skeletal system.
> They are the frame that gives your shape and some are big and some are little.
> Bones are alive and they will mend if broken parts are kept together.
> Some bones have joints so they can bend, and some make
> > red blood cells in the marrow.
> So drink your milk and keep strong bones for your skeletal system.

> **The Bones**
> The head (cranium, mandible);
> The trunk (scapula, clavicle, sternum, vertebrae, ribs, and pelvis);
> The arm (humerus, ulna, radius);
> The hand (carpals, metacarpals, phalanges);
> The leg (femur, patella, tibia, fibula);
> And the foot (tarsals, metatarsals, and phalanges).

ACTIVITY: Broken bones are very painful and need to have medical attention. It would be best to avoid broken bones by being careful. However, there are occasions when bones get broken anyway. Let's practice some broken bone "first aid" today so that you can be prepared to help someone with a broken bone.

Let's divide into teams of two. Each team member will take turns having a "broken" wrist and the other will help him. When a bone is broken, the first thing to do is to keep it "stable." This means to keep the broken pieces from moving around. You can use a magazine, piece of cardboard, or even a folded towel to make a support or "splint." You will also need a "sling." This could be something such as a dish-towel or a baby blanket. It needs to be long enough to go under the arm and fasten behind the neck. Fold the material diagonally. Carefully slide the support under the injured area. Using the splint, support the wrist and put the sling underneath it, with the folded edge supporting the hand and wrist. Fasten the sling behind the neck. Also, it is good to put ice over the injured area to keep it from swelling. Put the ice in a plastic bag or wrap it in a washcloth. Carefully place it on the wrist. Pretend to take the person to the doctor. Then, trade roles.

BIBLE READING: *(Have student look up Scriptures.)* Bones are important to us. They provide structure and protection for our bodies. We don't really think about which bone is bigger than the other or which bone is more important. We need them all! And we don't even notice them unless they are broken. God's commandments provide the framework and protection we need for our spiritual lives. We need them all! And we don't even notice how well they are working to give us structure and protection unless they are broken. Let's read them together and talk about how they apply to our lives (Exodus 20:1–17). If we try to obey the commandments without having the right attitudes, the commandments become dead and weighty to us, like the exoskeleton of the insects (Matthew 5:17–19, 5:21–24, 19:16–20, 22:35–40). But if they are a part of our lives and we follow them out of love for God, they are alive and our understanding of them grows and grows. (Matthew 11:28–30; John 8:31–32).

NOTEBOOK: *God Made Me, pp. 217-226.* You will be working with the *God Made Me* pages for several lessons. Start by assembling the body outline as directed with *God Made Me (pages 1, 2, and 3).* Then cut out the "bones" and glue them as directed. Glue only the flapped edge of the cranium and the ribs so that these can be lifted back later when we add the internal organs. Learn the names of the bones as you work with them. [*Over the next few weeks, have the student memorize the names of the bones by working through them from head to toe; the head (cranium, mandible); the trunk (scapula, clavicle, sternum, vertebrae, ribs, pelvis); the arm (humerus, ulna, radius); the hand (carpals, metacarpals, phalanges); the leg (femur, patella, tibia, fibula); the foot (tarsals, metatarsals, phalanges).*]

EVOLUTION STUMPERS: The total number of bones evolutionists use to demonstrate the development of the human from the ape could easily fit into a single coffin. Some of the bones that were once thought to be parts of human evolution were later found to be a pig's tooth, a small piece of an ape's jawbone and so forth. Also, more recent discoveries (at Glenn Rose, TX) have found human footprints on top of dinosaur footprints imbedded in the same layer of rock. Would you feel confident in basing major scientific conclusions on just a coffin-sized box of mixed bones?

REVIEW: 1. What are two functions of bones? [*to provide a framework for the body; to protect delicate organs; to manufacture red blood cells*]
2. Where are red blood cells produced? [*in the marrow of the long bones*]
3. Which bones protect your lungs and heart? [*ribs*]
4. Which bones protect your brain? [*cranium or skull*]
5. Are bones living tissue or dead tissue?   [*living*]

Have the student explain his notebook page to a friend or relative and tell what he learned from the lesson.

DIGGING DEEPER: 1. Continue reading *Fearfully and Wonderfully Made*, by Dr. Paul Brand & Phillip Yancy, Zondervan Publishing House, Grand Rapids, MI, 1980. 2. Summarize, in an outline form, the preparation and requirements needed to become a chiropractor. 3. Fill out a *Scientist Detective* page for Leonardo da Vinci (1452-1519) and what he discovered about the human body. 4. Study some diseases that affect the bones, such as osteoarthritis, osteomyelitis or Multiple Myeloma. 5. Research discoveries about x-rays by Wilhelm Konrad von Roentgen (1845-1923) or Arthur Holly Compton (1892-1962), and the discovery of radium by Marie and Pierre Curie (1850's - 1930's). Compare the modern-day use of x-rays, MRI and CAT scans.

LESSON 30: Man—Digestive System

PREPARATION: *You will need a long tube sock and a baseball (or similar size ball) for the activity. Student will need* **notebook pp. 227-231, 233-234**, *crayons, scissors, glue and a pencil. Vocabulary words may be written on flash cards.*

VOCABULARY:
> **digestion**: to prepare food to be absorbed into the blood [L. *digerere*, to arrange]
> **esophagus:** the tube from the mouth to the stomach [L. *oesophagus*, esophagus]
> **gall bladder:** the small sac which stores bile produced by liver [O.E. *gealla*, gall + *blaedre*, a blister]
> **intestines:** the bowels, the tubing from the stomach to the anus [L. *intestinus*, intestines]
> **liver**: the organ which secretes bile [O.E. *lifer*, liver]
> **pancreas:** the digestive gland behind the stomach [Gk. *pan*, all + *kreas*, flesh]
> **peristalsis:** rippling contractions of the muscles in the intestines
> **rectum:** lower portion of large intestines [L. *rectus*, straight]
> **stomach:** the chief organ of digestion [Gk. *stomachos*, the gullet]

INTRODUCTION: Digestive System. Have you ever used a blender or food processor? It takes a large piece of food and breaks it up into small pieces. This is similar to what happens in the beginning part of the digestive system. Our digestive system prepares food so that it can be absorbed into the blood and be used by the cells for energy.

SONG/POEM:

> **The Digestive System**
> The mouth is where we start with the digestive system.
> The teeth chew up the food and it goes down the esophagus
> Into the stomach where it's churned and fats and proteins are digested.
> Then in the small intestines nutrients get right into the blood
> And the large intestines pass wastes out of the digestive system.

NOTEBOOK: *God Made Me, p. 227-230* Glue the parts of the digestive system in place on your body outline. Don't forget the liver, gall bladder and pancreas! You couldn't digest food without them. These organs produce chemicals that help to break down food.

Digestive System, pp. 231, 233-234. I want you to discover what happens during digestion before we discuss it. Cut out the pieces of the puzzle on *Digestive System* *(page 2)* and glue them in place on the *Digestive System* page. Then write in the answers for "Where does it happen?" When you finish the page, tell me what happens at each step of digestion. [*The follow-up discussion should include these basic elements: We put food in our mouths, chew it up with our teeth while saliva softens and starts digesting carbohydrates. Then we swallow it down a tube called the* **esophagus**. *In our* **stomachs**, *various chemicals (acids and enzymes) are added, and the food is churned for about a half an hour. Most of the* **digestion** *takes place in the small* **intestines** *and from them the nutrients pass into the blood and are carried to each cell of the body to use for energy or fuel. The* **liver**, **gall bladder** *and* **pancreas** *produce chemicals that aid in this digestion. The parts that can't be used are pushed out of our body through the large intestines and rectum.*]

[**Answers:** *Where does it happen?*

1. *nose/mouth*
    a. *smells*
    b. *tastes*
2. *mouth*
    a. *saliva moistens*
    b. *teeth chew*
    c. *carbohydrates break down into sugars*
3. *esophagus (tube food travels down from mouth to stomach)*
4. *stomach*
    a. *churns half hour*
    b. *acid (hydrochloric) breaks down protein*
    c. *lipase breaks down fats*
5. *small intestines*
    a. *food breaks down into nutrients*
    b. *millions of villi pick up nutrients and put them into the blood*
6. *large intestines*
    a. *unusable food moves on*
    b. *water is removed*
    c. *remainder passes out of body*]

ACTIVITY: Food moves through the intestines by a process called **peristalsis**. The rings of muscles in the approximately fifteen feet of tubing in your intestines, contract or tighten behind the mass of food so that it can ripple on through. Fiber, such as grains and vegetables, are very important in this process.

Let's pretend that this ball is your food. Put it in the toe part of a long tube sock and squeeze the end of the sock behind the ball. With each squeeze, the ball moves a little further along the sock until it eventually comes out. The muscles in your intestines squeeze the food along in a similar way.

BIBLE READING: *(Have student look up Scriptures.)* Food is something that we all need to have. If you don't have food, eventually you will starve to death. Some people are worried about food all the time. They worry that it isn't clean or that they won't have enough. Jesus told us not to worry about what we eat, but instead to be concerned about what we think and do (Matthew 15:16–20). And He also told us not to worry about getting food (Matthew 6:24–34). There are many examples of how God miraculously provided food; the manna in the wilderness (Exodus 16:4), the oil and flour that never ran out (1 Kings 17:9–16), and the feeding of the five thousand (Luke 9:12–17). But even though it is necessary for the body to have food, it is also necessary to feed our spirits.

When Jesus had fasted for forty days and nights in the wilderness, Satan tempted Him by asking Him to turn stones into bread. Jesus responded by saying that man shall not live by bread alone but by every word of God (Matthew 4:4; Deuteronomy 8:3). He also said that we shouldn't work for food that rots and spoils, but for eternal food (John 6:27). Jesus told us that He Himself was the true manna, or bread of heaven, and that if we believe in Him and do His will we will live with Him forever (John 6:48–58).

SONG/POEM:

It's Not What You're Eating

You're restless and weary, you can't sleep at night.
Your ulcer is hurting, your weight isn't right.
You eat brown bread and veggies, and a soft drink or two
Well, it's not what you're eating, it's what's eating on you.

It's not what you're eating, it's what's eating on you.
It's the thoughts that you're thinking that make you feel blue.
It's the sinning and heartache, a bottled feeling or two.
Well, it's not what you're eating, it's what's eating on you.

Friend, things could be different if you're willing to start,
Just erase the feelings and clean up your heart.
By looking above you and letting Jesus take hold,
He'll change what's eating on you, and He'll carry your load.

It's not what you're eating, it's what's eating on you.
It's the thoughts that you're thinking that make you feel blue.
It's the sinning and heartache, a bottled feeling or two.
Well, it's not what you're eating, it's what's eating on you.

REVIEW: 1. What do our teeth and saliva do? [*the teeth chew up food; saliva softens and begins digestion of carbohydrates*]

2. What tube does the food go down to get to the stomach? [*esophagus*]
3. What occurs in the stomach? [*acids and enzymes are added and food is churned*]
4. Where does most of digestion take place? [*in the small intestines*]
5. How are nutrients carried to all parts of the body? [*through the blood*]
6. Where does unusable food go? [*it is pushed out through the large intestines and rectum*]

Have the student explain his notebook page to a friend or relative and tell what he learned from the lesson. Also, review the songs/poems and activities.

DIGGING DEEPER: 1. Fill out a *Scientist Detective* page for Dr. William Beaumont (1785–1853) and find out about the fascinating way that this American army doctor was able to study digestion from his patient, Alexis St. Martin. (*The Dictionary of American Biography*, Scribners, NY, Ed. Allen Johnson, 1929, has a good account.) 2. Figure out at least two balanced meals, taking the food pyramid into account. Do the planning, shopping and cooking for the meals. 3. Experience meals from another culture. Read and prepare a meal from the Mennonite cookbook, *Extending the Table...A World Community Cookbook*, by Joetta H. Schlabach, Herald Press, Scottdale, PA, 1991. 4. Read portions from Chapters 7 to 18 of *The Forever Feast*, by Dr. Paul Brand, Vine Books, Servant Publications, Ann Arbor, MI, 1993. 5. Study the biblical dietary laws and how they might apply today. (Two good resources in this area are: *God's Key to Health and Happiness*, by Elmer A. Josephson, Fleming H. Revell, A division of Baker Book House, Grand Rapids, MI 49506, 1996, and *Health Begins in Him, Biblical Steps to Optimal Health and Nutrition*, by Terry Dorain, Huntington House, Lafayette, LA, 1995.)

LESSON 31: Man—Circulatory System

PREPARATION: *You will need a watch with a second hand. Student will need* **notebook p. 229-230**, *crayons, scissors, glue and a pencil. Vocabulary words may be written on flash cards.*

VOCABULARY:

arteries: blood vessels going away from the heart [Gk. *arteria*, an artery]

blood: the red, slightly thick (viscous) liquid that circulates in man and animals [O.E. *blod*, blood]

capillaries: network of tiny blood vessels connecting arteries and veins [L. *capillus*, hair]

heart: a special muscle that pumps blood to all parts of the body [O.E. *heorte*, heart]

plasma: the liquid part of your blood that carries the food to each cell [Gk. *plasma* from *plassein*, to form or mold]

platelets: plate-shaped cells that help to seal off broken blood vessels [Gk. *platus*, broad, flat]

red corpuscles: red blood cells, the part of the blood that carries oxygen to the cells and carbon dioxide away from the cells [L. *corpusculum*, a small body]

veins: blood vessels going toward the heart [L. *vene*, vein]

white corpuscles: white blood cells which serve to fight infection [L. *corpusculum*, a small body]

INTRODUCTION: Circulatory System. This system includes the blood, blood vessels, heart and lymphatic system. It connects all the parts of your body. The **heart** is a special muscle that acts as a pump. It pumps the blood all around your body, from your head to your toes, in a single minute. Your heart started beating eight months before you were born and will continue to beat about once a second until you die. The sixty thousand miles of blood vessels in your body are involuntary (or automatic) smooth muscles. They help to regulate your body temperature by tightening (or constricting) when it is cold and your body needs to save the warmth. When it is hot, they open wider (or expand) to allow heat to escape. This keeps the inside of your body at the same temperature (98.6°F) year round regardless of the weather. The vessels going away from the heart are called **arteries**, while the ones going toward the heart are called **veins**. They are connected by a network of tiny vessels called **capillaries**.

Blood looks like a red, slightly thick liquid to us, but under a microscope you could see that it has many parts. The biggest part of the blood is made up of red blood cells (or **red corpuscles**). The red blood cells, which look like discs, are largely responsible for carrying oxygen to each part of your body and also carrying away the carbon dioxide. Look at the blood veins in your arm. What color are they? [*blue*] This is because the blood in them is carrying off carbon dioxide, which makes the red blood cells have a blue color. In the lungs, the carbon dioxide will be exchanged for oxygen. As soon as the red blood cells get oxygen, they lose the blue color and are red again. Can you figure out why we only see red blood when we get a cut and are bleeding? [*When we cut ourselves, the blood comes in contact with the oxygen in the air immediately and turns the cells red.*] **Plasma**, the liquid part of your blood, carries the food (nutrients—minerals and proteins) to each cell. White blood cells (or **white corpuscles**) are another special type of cells in your blood. Their job is to fight germs and their number increases when they are needed to fight. **Platelets** help to seal off blood vessels when they are broken or injured. These are just a few of the types of cells in the blood. Maybe you will be the one to discover the purpose of some of the other cells! All of the answers are not in yet!

SONG/POEM:

The Circulatory System
The heart is where we start with the circulatory system.
The heart pumps blood around. Through arteries the blood will pound
Taking food and air to cells in every square inch of your body.
Then veins take wastes away through lungs and kidneys when you're healthy
Taking blood back to the heart in the circulatory system.

ACTIVITY: There are several places in your body where you can feel each beat of the heart. This beating is called your pulse. The easiest places to feel it are in your neck, just to the left or right of your windpipe, and in your wrist, in a straight line up from your thumb. You can feel your pulse if you firmly place your index and middle fingers over these spots. See if you can find your pulse right now. *(You will need a timer or a watch with a second hand.)* You can know how fast your heart is beating by counting the number of beats in 6 seconds and multiplying by 10 (or count for 30 seconds and multiply by 2). Count your pulse right now. I will tell you when to begin and when to stop. Write down your pulse. Now, run in place for two minutes. Then we will take your pulse again. How much faster did your heart beat when you were exercising? You can make your heart stronger by exercising regularly.

Here is another "first aid" tip for you to remember. If someone is bleeding, the best way to stop it is to hold firm pressure directly over the area. A clean washcloth, shirt, or towel under your hand will help to keep the cut cleaner. In addition, if the bleeding is on the arms or legs, elevate the area so that it is higher than the heart. If the nose is bleeding, hold pressure with your thumb and index fingers on both sides of the nose, just below the "bridge" (the "hard" part) for five minutes.

BIBLE READING: *(Have student look up Scriptures.)* Blood is mentioned over 200 times in the Bible. In a physical sense, blood is described as life: The life of the flesh is in the blood (Leviticus 17:11,13). In a spiritual sense, blood was used in exchange for forgiveness of sin. A life (signified by its blood) was given in exchange for another life. The blood of the sacrificed lamb protected the first-born Israelites from death (Exodus 12:21–32). But the blood sacrifices in the Old Testament were just a picture of the ultimate sacrifice. Jesus shed His blood, dying on the cross, in exchange (or payment) for the death penalty we deserve because of our sin (Hebrews 9: 6–15). The blood of Jesus cleanses us from sin (1 John 1:6–10). Jesus asked us to remember His sacrifice by taking the Lord's Supper (Luke 22:17–20; John 6:53–58).

NOTEBOOK: *God Made Me, p. 229-230.* Using the body outline you prepared before, cut out the heart and glue it under the ribs, slightly to the left side of the middle. Then color it red.

EVOLUTION STUMPERS: DNA (the building blocks of chromosomes which house the genes) is found in the nucleus of all living cells with the exception of the red blood cells and a few viruses. It is billed by scientists as the "mysterious basis of ALL life." [Yet this "mysterious" element is not found in the blood, which God's word identifies as where life is (Leviticus 17:11).] Why isn't DNA in red blood cells? Why can't life be injected into something that is not alive with just a shot of DNA?

REVIEW: 1. What is the job of the heart? [*to pump blood to every part of the body*]
2. Name three types of blood vessels. [*arteries, veins, capillaries*]
3. What is the job of red corpuscles? [*carry oxygen to cells, carry carbon dioxide away*]
4. What do the white corpuscles do? [*fight infection*]
5. What are platelets for? [*seal off broken blood vessels*]
6. What is plasma and what does it do? [*liquid part of blood, carries nutrients to cells*]

Have the student explain his notebook page to a friend or relative and tell what he learned from the lesson. Also, review the songs/poems and activities.

DIGGING DEEPER: 1. Interview a nurse or a doctor about the blood. Find out what factors need to be considered when giving a blood transfusion, what diseases are carried in the blood and how the heart works. 2. Learn to do CPR (cardio-pulmonary resuscitation). 3. Fill out a *Scientist Detective* page for William Harvey (1578–1657) or Marcello Malpighi (1628–1694) who both studied the circulatory system. 4. Watch the video, *Red River of Life*, from Moody Institute of Science, 820 N. La Salle Blvd, Chicago, IL, 60610, 1995. 5. Study blood disorders such as hemophilia, anemia and sickle cell anemia. 6. Read the chapters on "Blood" (4-8) from *In His Image*, by Dr. Paul Brand & Phillip Yancy, Zondervan Publishing House, Grand Rapids, MI, 1984.

LESSON 32: Man—Respiratory System

PREPARATION: *Student will need **notebook p. 229-230 (from last lesson)**, crayons, scissors, glue and a pencil. Vocabulary words may be written on flash cards.*

VOCABULARY:
>**alveoli:** tiny air cells in the lungs [L. *alveolus*, a small cavity]
>**trachea:** the windpipe or tube in the throat which connects the mouth and nose
>to the lungs [Gk. *tracheia*, windpipe]

INTRODUCTION: Respiratory System. All parts of our body need a gas found in the air to be able to work. What part of the air does your body need? [*oxygen*] How do you get air into your body? [*by breathing*] Air enters through our nose or mouth and goes down into our lungs through the **trachea**. The muscles of the diaphragm, which are right under your ribs, help to pump air in and out of the lungs. Our lungs have thousands of tiny sacs called **alveoli**, which are similar to tiny balloons. Each time we breathe in, we fill them up with air. The air enters the blood stream and is carried to each cell. Our cells need oxygen to burn to make the energy they need to work. After they use the oxygen, they give off a waste gas called carbon dioxide. This is passed back into the blood, carried to the lungs, and we breathe it out.

Do you know what day you took your very first breath? The first breath you took was the moment you were born. Up until then you didn't need to breathe. You got oxygen from your mother's blood through your umbilical cord. How many times do you breathe every minute? Just breathe normally and we'll count your respirations (the number of breaths you take) for 30 seconds and multiply that by two. *(You will need a timer or a watch with a second hand.)* [Children breathe about 20 times every minute. Adults breathe 12–16 times a minute.] When we run or exercise, our body needs more oxygen so we have to breathe faster. Also, if we are sick, our body is working harder and we breathe faster.

SONG/POEM:
>**The Respiratory System**
>The nose is where we start with the respiratory system.
>The air comes in and then goes down the trachea into the lungs
>Where oxygen is then released into the circulatory system.
>Carbon dioxide is returned into the air and then breathed out
>Back through the nose and through the mouth in the respiratory system.

ACTIVITY: Try to hold your breath as long as you can. I'll count the seconds aloud and you can write down how many seconds you held your breath. You can practice holding it longer when you are swimming, but you will still have to breathe within a few minutes no matter how much practice you have. Your body, and especially your brain, cannot live without oxygen for more than a few minutes. Respiration is controlled automatically and when you hold your breath, the urge to breathe again is very strong.

BIBLE READING: *(Have student look up Scriptures.)* When God formed man from the dust of the earth, he was not alive until God breathed the breath of life into his nose (Genesis 2:7;

Job 27:3, 33:4). In your physical body, you can go without food for weeks without dying. You can go without water for days. But you cannot go without breathing for more than just a few minutes. In your spirit, you cannot be fully alive without God's breath (or His Spirit) within you. Ezekiel had an astounding vision in the valley of the dry bones and you can read about the importance of God's breath in Ezekiel 37:1-14.

SONG/POEM:

> **Fill Our Hearts**   (Andrew's Song)
> Lord, let me love with open hand,
> This child you gave to me,
> May he learn of your love through mine,
> And seek your child to be.
> Lord, guide me step by step to know,
> The way to show my son,
> That you and you alone, dear Lord,
> Are everything in one.
>
> Lord, may I show him day by day,
> To put you first in line.
> So by example, he can learn,
> To have a Friend like mine.
> As we rise up and walk together,
> As we go to sleep,
> May you, Lord Jesus fill our hearts,
> For they are yours to keep.

NOTEBOOK: *God Made Me, p. 229-230.* Color, cut out, and glue the lungs onto the *God Made Me* page.

REVIEW: 1. How important is breathing? [*critically important—the brain and body can't live without oxygen for more than a few minutes*]
2. Where does air enter the respiratory system? [*through the mouth and nose*]
3. What purpose does the trachea serve? [*it is the passageway for air to the lungs*]
4. What are alveoli? [*tiny air sacs in the lungs*]
5. What waste gas do we breathe out? [*carbon dioxide*]

TEST: *Student will need* **notebook p. 255,** *Crossword Review 11. Use as a review or test for older students.* **Answers:** *Teacher's p. 128.*

Have the student explain his notebook page to a friend or relative and tell what he learned from the lesson.

DIGGING DEEPER: 1. Study how CPR (cardio-pulmonary resuscitation) relates to the respiratory system. 2. Find out what inventions have allowed people to continue to breathe where there is no oxygen available (e.g., respirators, aqua lungs, space suits, and so forth). 3. Visit a hospital and see what can be used to help people breathe when they are not able to breathe by themselves (ventilators, IPPB and so forth). 4. Study diseases that affect the respiratory system, such as tuberculosis, asthma and emphysema. 5. Read Chapter 14, "Breath" from *In His Image*, by Dr. Paul Brand & Phillip Yancy, Zondervan Publishing House, Grand Rapids, MI, 1984.

LESSON 33: Man—Nervous System

PREPARATION: *You will need an ice cube, a cotton ball, a spoon, a warmed washcloth and as many other different items as are available for touch awareness activity. Student will need notebook pp. 232-235.*

VOCABULARY:
>   **autonomic:** self-governing [Gk. *autos*, self + *nomos*, a law]
>   **nerve:** fiber which sends or receives messages from the brain [L. *nervus*, sinew]
>   **parasympathetic:** a part of the nervous system that controls involuntary vital
>   functions in an energy-conserving way [Gk. *para*, beside + *sun*,
>   together + *pathos*, feeling]
>   **sympathetic:** a portion of the nervous system that controls involuntary vital functions
>   and the "fight or flight" response [Gk. *sun*, together + *pathos*, feeling]

INTRODUCTION: Nervous System. The nervous system is like the body's communication system. Tiny **nerve** receptors are underneath your skin and they send electrical messages to your brain to tell it when they feel hot or cold, soft or hard, and many other things. The brain sends messages through the spinal cord to the nerves to tell the muscles what to do—for example, it tells the arm muscles to pull the fingers away from the hot stove.

SONG/POEM:

The Nervous System
The brain is where we start with the central nervous system.
The nerves are hooked up to the skin and send the message to the brain
Telling if it's hot or cold and if it hurts or if it feels good.
The brain then sends a message back and gives a warning if there's danger,
Keeping skin and body safe with the nervous system.

The brain is where we start with the autonomic nervous system.
The nerves send messages along, so heart and lungs will function strong.
And all the vital organs work without a conscious thought or effort.
The nerves say slow it down or speed it up, be ready if there's danger,
So you stay healthy and alive with the autonomic nervous system

ACTIVITY: Close your eyes and I want you to pick up several different objects, one at a time. I want you to tell me as much as you can about them without looking. *(Use an ice cube, a cotton ball, a spoon, a warmed washcloth and as many other different items as are available.)* How could you know what you were touching when you couldn't even see it? What are some of the different types of things you noticed about the different items? [*temperature, texture, etc.*]

BIBLE READING: *(Have student look up Scriptures.)* Humans sometimes consider themselves very wise and smart. But do you know what the Bible has to say about the world's wisdom? Look it up in Romans 1:22, Proverbs 3:7, Luke 10:21 and 1 Corinthians 3:18–20. On the other hand, growing in God's wisdom should be our goal (Luke 2:52; James 1:5; Proverbs 8). Jesus tells several parables about the wise and the foolish. Read about them and think about ways that you can be wise by God's standards (Matthew 7:24–27, 25:1–13; Luke 12:16–21).

SONG/POEM:

If Everybody Does it, We Don't

Mom, my friend has a new toy that I want.
Dad, the guys are all goin' to camp.
Grandma, nobody now can believe that!
You're not cool and neither is Gramp.

Well, son, the Lord has called us to be different,
We can't just go along with the crowd,
So the best guidelines that we can think of,
Is to not do what most are allowed. **So—**

If everybody does it, we don't,
If everybody has it, we won't,
If everybody's goin', we'll go the other way,
If everybody does it, we don't.

NOTEBOOK: *The Human Brain, pp. 232-234. (With younger children, do together as a class.)* The human brain is fabulously complex. No computer can come close to competing with your brain. Your brain is able to control all the automatic things that go on in your body without you ever thinking about them. You never have to tell your brain to make your heart beat or your stomach to churn or your lungs to breathe. Your brain also responds to your thoughts. You can think about moving your arm, and your brain will send a message to your arm to move. You can think about eating and your brain gets your salivary glands prepared. Through much research and study, some general areas of the brain have been mapped out. Two of these maps are on your page for you to discover. Color and cut out the pieces from *The Human Brain (page 2)*. Glue them in place. Then draw lines from the part of the brain (where the words are) to the area of the body that it controls (on the body drawn above it). *(Draw a line from the toe to the word "toe", and so forth.)*

Automatic Pilot, p. 235. A lot of body functions happen all the time without you having to even think about them. The part of the nervous system that controls the body's automatic vital functions (heart beating, breathing, digestion, and so forth) is called the **autonomic** nervous system. There are two sets of nerves that work together to keep the vital functions of your body in operation. These are the **parasympathetic** nerves and the **sympathetic** nerves. Overall, the parasympathetic nerves try to conserve your body's energy. The sympathetic nerves use energy and are an important part of your body's emergency plan. When danger threatens, the sympathetic nerves shut down non-essential functions and prepare you for "fight or flight." Draw a line from each automatic body function to where the message originates in the spine, using the information at the bottom of the page. You may check the boxes when you have used that answer. Draw red lines for (A), the parasympathetic nerves located in the neck, blue lines for (B), the sympathetic nerves located in your spine, and use green lines for (C), the parasympathetic nerves located in your lower spine.

REVIEW: 1. What is the purpose of the nerves?   [*to send and receive messages from the brain*]

2. What types of messages do they send to the brain? [*temperature, texture, pain, pleasure*]

3. What part of the brain is the center for movement and sensation? [*cerebrum; somatosensory cortex*]

4. What part of the nervous system controls the body's automatic functions? [*the autonomic nervous system*]

Have the student explain his notebook page to a friend or relative and review the songs.

DIGGING DEEPER: 1. Fill out a Scientist Detective page for pediatric neurosurgeons Dr. Fred Epstein (has been featured in *Reader's Digest* magazine at least twice) or Dr. Ben Carson. Dr. Carson's autobiography is *Gifted Hands* by Ben Carson, M.D., Zondervan Publishing House, Grand Rapids, MI, 1990. 2. Read the book or watch the video of how Joni Eareckson Tada was paralyzed in a diving accident, *Joni*, World Wide Pictures, Inc., 1979. (The film is rated PG, so you might want to preview it first, especially if you have young children.) 3. Read the chapters on "Head" (9-13), Chapter 16, "Go Between" and the chapters on "Pain" (19-23) from *In His Image*, by Dr. Paul Brand & Phillip Yancy, Zondervan Publishing House, Grand Rapids, MI, 1984.

LESSON 34: Man—Integumentary System

PREPARATION: *Student will need* **notebook pp. 236-237, 239-240,** *crayons, scissors, glue and pencil. You will need three plastic bowls, one with hot water, one with cold water, and one with lukewarm water. Vocabulary words may be written on flash cards.*

VOCABULARY:
> **adipose tissue** : fatty tissue [L. *adeps*, soft fat]
> **dermis** : living layer of skin below epidermis [Gk. *derma*, the skin]
> **epidermis:** outer layer of skin, made up of dead cells [Gk. *epi*, upon + *derma*, the skin]
> **hair follicle:** gland which produces thread-like growth [O.E. *haer*, hair +
>   L. *folliculus*, a little bag]
> **integumentary:** protective layer of tissue covering body [L. *integere*, to cover]
> **oil gland:** cells which produce a greasy liquid [L. *oleum*, oil]
> **sweat gland:** cells which produce perspiration or moisture from skin
>   [O.E. *swat*, sweat + L. *glans*, an acorn]

INTRODUCTION: Integumentary System. Your skin has the important job of covering and protecting your body. There are three layers of skin. The outer covering is called the **epidermis**, then comes the **dermis** and last is the **adipose tissue** or fatty layer. These layers all work together to protect your body from germs, to keep your body temperature right, to remove some wastes, and to give you the sense of touch. Your skin contains **sweat glands**, **oil glands**, and **hair follicles**.

SONG/POEM:

Skin Deep (Abby's Song)
If you see a pretty face walking down the street
Remember, it's just skin deep,
If you think someone's good looking from their head to their feet
Remember, it's just skin deep.
But if someone does a good deed and their words are true
What they're like inside is really coming through

So let your outside in
Be like your inside out
And let God's love shine through in all you do.
Don't let your focus stray
To things that fade away
And let God's love shine through in all you do.

If you spend a lot of hours to fix your outside up
Remember, it's just skin deep,
If you look into a mirror and want to cover up
Remember, it's just skin deep,
But if you can do a good deed and your words are true
What you're like inside is really coming through.

So let your outside in
Be like your inside out
And let God's love shine through in all you do.
Don't let your focus stray
To things that fade away
And let God's love shine through in all you do.

ACTIVITY: *(You will need three plastic bowls, one with hot water, one with ice-cold water, and one with lukewarm water.)*   The heat and cold sense receptors in your hands can't tell the exact temperature, but can give you a comparison. Put your left hand in the hot water and your right hand in the cold water. Leave them there for a minute. Now, put both hands in the lukewarm water at the same time. Describe what each hand feels. Does it differ?

BIBLE READING: *(Have student look up Scriptures.)*   The skin does many important jobs to help keep your body healthy and safe. The skin is your contact with the outside world and when you stub your toe or burn your finger, the nerve endings in your skin send the message for you to move away from danger. Leprosy (and diabetes) destroys these nerves so that they are no longer sensitive. This results in damage to the body because no pain was felt before injury has occurred. In the Bible there are many stories of lepers (2 Kings 5:1–14). They were isolated from everyone because of their dreaded disease (Leviticus 13:45–46). Jesus healed many of them (Luke 4:12–14, 17:12–19). What gives us warning of spiritual danger? The Holy Spirit, through our conscience warns us of danger and tells us what is right and wrong. When we ignore our conscience and do wrong things, we injure our conscience and make it less sensitive (Romans 1:21–32; 1 Corinthians 8:1–13; Ephesians 4:17–20; 1 Timothy 4:1–2). We can end up with damage not only to our spirits but also our physical bodies. Jesus can heal and restore a healthy conscience to us if we ask (Romans 12:1–2; Hebrews 9:13–14, 10:22; 1 Timothy 3:7–10; 1 Peter 3:15–17).

SONG/POEM:

Jesus Says So Lovingly

Her life was far from innocent, but when it came to change,
They still accused and threw their stones, now don't you think that's strange?
For Jesus to the woman said, "Child, go and sin no more,
"Your sins were blotted out to me, when you came in my door."
And Jesus said, so lovingly, "Go and sin no more."

He lived his life just as he pleased, he lived it for himself,
But when the master called, he came, and found a heavenly wealth.
And Jesus to the man did say, "Come unto me and live,
"Die to yourself and follow me, a brand new start I'll give."
And Jesus said, so lovingly, "A brand new start I'll give."

We all have ups, we all have downs, a war inside you'll find,
But grace abounds where Christ resides, let Him renew your mind.
And Jesus says to all who hear, "Love God and neighbor too,
"And show My love to everyone, in everything you do."
And Jesus says, so lovingly, "Show love in all you do."

NOTEBOOK: *Skin Deep, p. 236.* Your skin is fantastic. One square inch of skin has more going on than meets the eye. And your fingerprints are different from anyone else's. Follow the direction for the *Skin Deep* page and then we'll go over it together.

Fingerprint Detective Game, pp. 237, 239-240. Follow the directions for this game on the *Fingerprint Detective Game (page 2).* Have fun!

REVIEW: 1. What are three important functions of your skin? [*to protect your body from germs, to keep your body temperature right, to remove some wastes, and to give you the sense of touch*]
2. Why can fingerprints be used to identify a person? [*everyone's are unique*]

Have the student explain his notebook page to a friend or relative and tell what he learned from the lesson. Also, review the songs/poems and activities.

DIGGING DEEPER: 1. Study the effects of damage to the skin, such as bruises, cuts, or burns (1st, 2nd and 3rd degree). Learn how to prevent and care for these emergencies. 2. Learn how detectives are able to identify suspects by the fingerprints left at the scene of a crime. 3. Learn proper skin care (washing, protecting from sun or chemicals, modest use of make-up and so forth). 4. Watch the video, *Windows of the Soul,* (about the 5 senses) from Moody Institute of Science, 820 N. La Salle Blvd, Chicago, IL, 60610, 1995. 5. Read Chapter 2, "Mirror" from *In His Image,* by Dr. Paul Brand & Phillip Yancy, Zondervan Publishing House, Grand Rapids, MI, 1984.

LESSON 35: Man—Endocrine System and Excretory System

PREPARATION: *Student will need* **notebook p. 229-230 (from Lesson 31),** *crayons, scissors, glue and pencil. Vocabulary words may be written on flash cards.*

VOCABULARY:

bladder: a muscular bag in the pelvis that collects the urine [O.E. *blaedre*, a blister]

endocrine system: tissues and organs that produce internal secretions called hormones [Gk. *endon*, within + *krinein*, to separate]

excretory system: the parts that expel wastes from the body [L. *excernere*, to sift out]

kidneys: a pair of organs that excrete urine

ureter: the tubes from the kidneys to the bladder [Gk. *ouron*, urine]

urine: the yellow-colored liquid that contains water soluble wastes from the body [Gk. *ouron*, urine]

INTRODUCTION: Endocrine System. Special organs produce chemicals called hormones that control many functions deep inside your body. These control such things as how much you grow and how the food you eat is digested and used. The glands in this system include the pituitary, the thyroid, the parathyroid, the reproductive organs, the adrenal, and the pancreas.

Excretory System. The parts of our body that get rid of wastes are known as the excretory system. You have studied some of these parts already. When you studied the digestive system, you learned about the large intestines and rectum that dispose of the solid wastes (bowel movement). When you studied the integumentary system, you discovered that the sweat glands get rid of some wastes through the skin and also help to cool the body (perspiration). With every breath you exhale, the lungs excrete the waste carbon dioxide. The final part of the excretory system is the urinary tract, which includes the **kidneys**, **ureters**, and **bladder**, and cleanses the body of water-soluble wastes called "**urine**." Tiny tubes in the kidneys filter wastes out of the blood stream. These wastes flow through the ureters to the bladder and are excreted as urine from your body. When any of these systems get out of order, they can result in serious problems. Drinking six to eight glasses of water a day helps keep your body clean from the inside out.

BIBLE READING: *(Have student look up Scriptures.)* There are certain parts of our body that are private parts. We don't show them or talk about them with just anyone. And yet they are very important to us. If wastes build up in your body, they can become toxic (poisonous) to you. In the body of Christ, the Church, some people have behind-the-scene type jobs that don't show and can't be shared with just anyone (such as counseling, helping people "clean up" their lives, settling arguments, doing spiritual warfare, and confronting evil wherever it is found). These people are vital for the good of the whole body. Let's read 1 Corinthians 12:12-31 and 13 and see how each member of Christ's body functions together.

SONG/POEM:

Speak up for the Lord (Amos' Song)
Speak up for the Lord,
Lift your voice and speak up for the Lord.
Every chance you get, tell of His love and grace,
To everyone everywhere.
Tell of His death, how He rose again,
And that He's coming back.
Speak up, yes, speak up for the Lord.

Speak out for the Lord,
Lift your voice and speak out for the Lord.
Tell the world what's wrong and what's right,
And that they need God's love and God's light.
Say, "Humble yourselves before the Lord,
Turn from your wicked ways."
And speak out, yes, speak out for the Lord.

Speak in to the Lord,
In your heart, just speak in to the Lord.
Say a prayer with each breath that you take,
All day and each moment that you're awake.
Speak in to the Lord,
In your heart, just speak in to the Lord.
Live your life to speak in, yes, speak in to the Lord.

NOTEBOOK: *God Made Me, p. 229-230.* Glue the remaining organs of the excretory system on the body, including the bladder, kidneys, and ureters.

REVIEW: 1. Name three glands of the endocrine system. [*the pituitary, the thyroid, the parathyroid, the reproductive organs, the adrenal, and the pancreas*]
2. What is the function of the excretory system? [*to get rid of wastes*]
3. What part of the digestive system also belongs to the excretory system? [*the large intestines and rectum*]
4. What part of the skin belongs to the excretory system? [*the sweat glands*]
5. What are three parts of the urinary tract? [*the kidneys, ureters, and bladder*]

Have the student explain his notebook page to a friend or relative and tell what he learned from the lesson. Also, review the songs/poems and activities.

DIGGING DEEPER: 1. Learn what to do for constipation or diarrhea. 2. Fill out a *Scientist Detective* page for Dr. Willem Kolff (1911–   ), inventor of the kidney dialysis machine and visit a kidney dialysis unit if possible. 3. Find out what deep-sea divers have to do in order to resurface. 4. Fill out a *Scientist Detective* page for Frederick Banting (1892–1941), the Canadian doctor who discovered insulin (a hormone produced by the pancreas).

LESSON 36: Man/ Muscular System

PREPARATION: *Student will need* **notebook pp. 241, 243-244,** *crayons, scissors, glue and a pencil. Vocabulary words may be written on flash cards.*

VOCABULARY:

extensors: muscles that extend or stretch out [l. *extendere*, to stretch out]
flexors: muscles that flex or bend up [l. *flexus*, bent]
involuntary muscles: muscles which work without conscious thought
muscle: a band of fibrous tissue that can produce movement [L. *musculus*, a muscle]
voluntary muscles: muscles we can move at will [L. *voluntas*, free will]

INTRODUCTION: Muscular System. You have about 600 muscles in your body. You can run and jump, write and talk. This all happens because of muscles you can control. These muscles are called the **voluntary** muscles, which means you can move them at will. You don't think about breathing, digesting an apple, or your heart beating, yet this all happens without your conscious direction. These muscles are the **involuntary** muscles, which means they work without your conscious thought. The skeletal muscles are voluntary muscles that connect to the bones and allow you to bend, lift, turn, and walk. The muscles of the heart (cardiac muscles) and smooth muscles (like the muscles in the stomach) are involuntary muscles and work without you telling them to.

SONG/POEM:

The Muscular System
The muscles are where we start with the muscular system,
The muscles are attached to bones,
So that the bones can move around.
And ligaments and tendons help to keep the muscle movements stable.
So exercise and make them strong and eat good meals at the table,
Then you can move and get around with your muscular system.

ACTIVITY: Let's do some exercises so that you can feel some of the muscles at work in your body. Muscles generally work in pairs—**extensors** extend or stretch out while **flexors** flex or bend up. Hold your left arm straight out in front of you. Now touch your left shoulder with your left hand. Put your right hand on top of your upper left arm while you are flexing your left arm and feel how that muscle changes. Lie on the floor and try to do a sit-up. Put hands on your abdominal muscles and feel how they tighten as you try to sit up. Now stand up again and try to bend over and touch the floor without bending your knees. Feel the muscles on the backs of your thighs and calves. How do they change when you stand back up? Regular exercise helps to make our muscles strong and lack of exercise can result in not being able to use some muscles at all.

BIBLE READING: *(Have student look up Scriptures.)* It is good to keep in shape physically, but it is much more important to stay in excellent spiritual condition. The apostle Paul often compared the Christian life to being physically prepared for a race (1 Corinthians 9:24-27, Galatians 5:7), or for war (Philippians 2:25; 2 Timothy 2:1-5) Jesus was our perfect example, and by focusing our attention on Him and His life, we can run the race of life with hope, strength and faith (Hebrews 12:1-3). We have at our disposal some very special equipment (Ephesians 6: 10-18; Hebrews 4:12-16). What is the goal that we should strive for? Find out in 2 Timothy 4:7, 8 and Revelation 22:10-14.

SONG/POEM:

Try, Try Again

Did you tie up your shoes with the first bow that you tied?
'Course not, you tried, tried again.
Did you learn to read and write with the first word that you spied?
'Course not, you tried, tried again.

So let's try, try again, yes, let's try, try again,
They say that practice makes perfect if you'll only try again.
Come on and try, try again.

Did you climb up the mountain with the first step that you took?
'Course not, you tried, tried again.
Did you make Thanksgiving dinner for the first meal that you cooked?
'Course not, you tried, tried again.

So let's try, try again, yes, let's try, try again,
They say that practice makes perfect if you'll only try again.
Come on and try, try again.

Have you learned to love the Lord your God and neighbor as yourself?
Not yet, but try, try again.
Have you realized that money doesn't count for heavenly wealth?
Not yet, but try, try again.

So let's try, try again, yes, let's try, try again,
They say that practice makes perfect if you'll only try again.
Come on and try, try again.

NOTEBOOK: *The Inside Story, pp. 241, 243-244.* You have now been introduced to each of the ten major systems of your body. It is amazing to realize how many parts work together to make you who you are. *The Inside Story* page is a review of the systems. Cut out and put the two figures on *The Inside Story (page 2)* together so that both top sides will be the muscles and both bottom sides will be blank. Then glue the blank sides on the outline of the figure on *The Inside Story* page. As you unfold the figure at different places, you will see three different aspects of the inside of your body. For the bones, draw in the rest of the bones on the blank side and then draw a line from them to their names. Next draw in the rest of the major blood vessels by looking at the figure with the blood vessels across from it. Then color, cut, and glue the organs in the correct places. The kidneys and bladder must be glued first and will be hidden from view. Draw a line from each organ to its name. For the muscles, draw in the matching muscles.

REVIEW: 1. What are voluntary muscles? [*muscles we can move at will*]
2. What are involuntary muscles? [*muscles that work without conscious thought or effort*]
3. What are the two kinds of muscles that work as a unit in your arm? [*flexors and extensors*]

TEST: *Student will need **notebook p. 256,** Crossword Review 12. Use as a review or test for older students. **Answers:** Teacher's p. 128.*

Have the student explain his notebook page to a friend or relative.

DIGGING DEEPER: 1. Demonstrate muscle control by doing a performance such as gymnastics, dance, piano, or soccer. Then explain what kind of practice it took to build your skills so that your muscles perform accurately and on cue. 2. Study several health problems that affect the muscles, such as paraplegia, Multiple Sclerosis, or Muscular Dystrophy. 3. Tour a weight training class and learn how to build strength in specific muscles. 4. Outline the requirements and job description of a physical therapist.

The End...
(or is it, "The Beginning?")

ADDITIONAL RESOURCE SUGGESTIONS

Games/Computer/Worksheets

Botany Coloring Book, by Paul Young, Harper Perennial, HarperCollins Publishers, Inc, 10 East 53rd St, New York, NY, 10022, 1982.

GeoSafari® Science (CD ROM)

Krill—A Whale of a Game from Ampersand Press, 750 Lake St., Port Townsend, WA, 98368.

Lyrical Life Science, Vol 1, 2 and 3 by Doug and Dorry Eldon, Lyrical Learning, 8008 Cardwell Hill, Corvallis, OR 97330, 1996. Science definitions set to familiar tunes, worksheets available.

Science Enrichment: A Homework Booklet (Grades 3-6); *Biology; Life Science; The Human Body,* Instructional Fair, Inc., Grand Rapids, MI, 1994 (These are a series of activity/labeling/fill-in-the-blank books that are good for additional resources but have very little instruction included.)

The Pollination Game from Ampersand Press, 750 Lake St., Port Townsend, WA, 98368.

Books

Astronomy and the Bible, Questions and Answers by Donald B. DeYoung, Baker Book House, Grand Rapids, MI, 1989.

The Astronomy Book, by Dr. Jonathan Henry, Master Books, Green Forest, AR, 1999.

Body by Design: The Anatomy and Physiology of the Human Body, by Alan L. Gillen, Master Books. Green Forest, AR, 2001.

Boy Scout Manuals

Charlotte's Web, by E.B. White.

Character Sketches from the Pages of Scripture Illustrated in the World of Nature, Vol. 1, 2, and 3, from the Institute in Basic Life Principles, Box 1, Oak Brook, IL 60522-3001.

Champions of Discovery Series, by John Hudson Tiner, Master Books, P. O. Box 727, Green Forest, AR, 72638.

1. Creation Anatomy: A Study Guide to the Miracles of the Body!, 2. Creation Astronomy: A Study Guide to the Constellations! 3. Creation Geology: A Study Guide to Fossils, Formations and the Flood! by Felice Gerwitz & Jill Whitlock, 4. *Truth Seekers* series by Christina & Felice Gerwitz, Media Angels, 15720 S. Pebble Lane, Fort Myers, FL, 33912-2341.

The Everyday Science Sourcebook, by Lawrence F. Lowery, Dale Seymour Publications, Palo Alto, CA 94303, 1985.

Exploring Series, by John Hudson Tiner, Master Books, P. O. Box 727, Green Forest, AR, 72638.

Extending the Table...A World Community Cookbook, by Joetta H. Schlabach, Herald Press, Scottdale, PA, 1991.

**Fearfully and Wonderfully Made,* by Dr. Paul Brand & Phillip Yancy, Zondervan Publishing House, Grand Rapids, MI, 1980.

The Forever Feast, by Dr. Paul Brand, Vine Books, Servant Publications, Ann Arbor, MI 1993.

*For Those Who Dare, 101 Great Christians and How They Changed The World,
by John Hudson Tiner, Master Books, Green Forest, AR, 2002.

The Geology Book, by Dr. John D. Morris, Master Books, Green Forest, AR, 2000.

Gifted Hands, by Ben Carson, M.D., Zondervan Publishing House, Grand Rapids, MI, 1990.

God's Key to Health and Happiness, by Elmer A. Josephson, Fleming H. Revell, A division of Baker
Book House, Grand Rapids, MI 49506, 1996.

The Gospel in the Stars, by Joseph A. Seiss, Kregel Publications, Grand Rapids, MI, 49501, 1972.

Health Begins in Him, Biblical Steps to Optimal Health and Nutrition, by Terry Dorain, Huntington
House, Lafayette, LA, 1995.

*In His Image, by Dr. Paul Brand & Phillip Yancy, Zondervan Publishing House, Grand Rapids,
MI, 1984.

In The Beginning: Compelling Evidence for Creation and the Flood, by Walt Brown, Center for
Scientific Creation, 5612 N. 20th Place, Phoenix, AZ, 85016, 1995.

Our Created Moon: Earth's Fascinating Neighbor, by Don B. DeYoung, Master Books, P. O. Box 727,
Green Forest, AR, 72638, 2003.

Red Cross First Aid Manual

Science and the Bible, by Henry M. Morris, Institute for Creation Research, 10946 Woodside Ave.
North, Santee, CA 92071.

Science in the Creation Week, by David Unfred, Noble Publishing Associates, Gresham, OR, 97030, 1994.

Sower Series, by John Hudson Tiner, Mott Media, 1000 East Huron Street, Milford, Michigan 48381.

The Usborne Illustrated Encyclopedia: The Natural World, EDC Publishing, 10302 E. 55th Place,
Tulsa, OK, 74146.

*Unlocking the Mysteries of Creation, by Dennis R. Petersen, Creation Resource Foundation, Box 570,
El Dorado, CA, 95623.

Usborne Encyclopedia of Planet Earth, EDC Publishing, 10302 E. 55th Place, Tulsa, OK, 74146.
(There are many beautiful Usborne science books to choose from. Usborne books do have
evolutionary references, but these can provide opportunity for discussion of creation.)

Your Guide to the Sky, by Rick Shaffer, Lowell House, Los Angeles, CA, 1994.

The Weather Book, by Michael Oard, Master Books, Green Forest, AR, 1997.

Videos

*Animal Kingdom, from Moody Institute of Science, 820 N. La Salle Blvd, Chicago, IL, 60610,
1995.

City of the Bees, from Moody Institute of Science, 820 N. La Salle Blvd, Chicago, IL, 60610.

Hidden Treasure, (rocks & minerals) from Moody Institute of Science, 820 N. La Salle Blvd,
Chicago, IL, 60610, 1995.

*Human Life, from Moody Institute of Science, 820 N. La Salle Blvd, Chicago, IL, 60610, 1995.

Joni, World Wide Pictures, Inc., 1979. (The film is rated PG, so preview it first, if you have young children.)

Journeys to the Edge of Creation: I. Our Solar System; II. The Milky Way & Beyond, produced by Moody Institute of Science, 820 N. LaSalle Blvd, Chicago, IL, 60610, 1996.

*Planet Earth, from Moody Institute of Science, 820 N. La Salle Blvd, Chicago, IL, 60610, 1995.

Red River of Life, (blood) from Moody Institute of Science, 820 N. La Salle Blvd, Chicago, IL, 60610, 1995.

Revealing Evidences for Creation, from Censored Science, 803 Coleman Dr., Plant City, FL, 33567

Roaring Waters, from Moody Institute of Science, 820 N. La Salle Blvd, Chicago, IL, 60610, 1995.

The Young Age of the Earth, AlphaProductions, 1994. Available from Earth Science Associates P.O.Box 12067, Knoxville, TN, 37912-0067.

Thundering Earth, from Moody Institute of Science, 820 N. La Salle Blvd, Chicago, IL, 60610, 1995.

Voice of the Deep or *Experience With an Eel*, from Moody Institute of Science, 820 N. La Salle Blvd, Chicago, IL, 60610, 1995.

Where Waters Run, from Moody Institute of Science, 820 N. La Salle Blvd, Chicago, IL, 60610.

Whirling Winds, from Moody Institute of Science, 820 N. La Salle Blvd, Chicago, IL, 60610, 1995.

Windows of the Soul, (about the 5 senses) from Moody Institute of Science, 820 N. La Salle Blvd, Chicago, IL, 60610, 1995.

*Priority purchases.

High School Science

Dr. Jay L. Wile

Apologia Educational Ministries
1106 Meridian Plaza Suite 220
Anderson, IN 46016 US
www.highschoolscience.com

SELECTED BIBLIOGRAPHY

ABC's of Nature, Pleasantville, New York: The Reader's Digest Association, Inc. 1984.

Amadon, Alfred Mason. *The Fold-Out Atlas of the Human Body.* New York: A Bonanza Pop-Up Book. 1984.

Arms, Karen, and Pamela S. Camp. *Biology.* New York: Holt, Rinehart, and Winston. 1979.

Asimov, Isaac. *On the Human Body and the Human Brain.* New York: Bonanza Books. 1963.

Barnet, Lincoln et. al. *The Sea.* New York: Golden Press. 1961.

Barnet, Lincoln, et al. *The World We Live In.* New York: Golden Press. 1962.

Bevans, Margaret ed., *The Golden Treasury of Knowledge.* New York: Golden Press. 1960.

Blackwood, Dr. Paul E., ed. *The Science Library.* New York: Grosset and Dunlap. 1970.

Brand, Dr. Paul, and Phillip Yancy. *Fearfully and Wonderfully Made.* Grand Rapids: Zondervan. 1980.

Branley, Franklyn M. *A Book of Planets for You.* New York: Scholastic Book Services. 1972.

Brown, Paula S. *The Incredible Body Machine.* New York: Random House/Children's Television Workshop. 1981.

Browne, Thomas, Ed., *The Mind Alive Encyclopedia, The Earth.* Great Britain: Chartwell Books Inc. 1977.

Burton, Dr. Maurice and Robert Burton, eds. *Funk and Wagnalls Wildlife Encyclopedia.* New York Funk and Wagnalls. 1969.

Carr, Archie. *The Reptiles.* New York: Time Incorporated. 1963.

Carrington, Richard. *The Mammals.* New York: Time Incorporated. 1963.

Character Sketches From the Pages of Scripture Illustrated in the World of Nature, Volume 1, Institute in Basic Life Principles Inc., Box 1, Oak Brook, IL 60522-3001, Rand McNally and Co., 1983.

Character Sketches From the Pages of Scripture Illustrated in the World of Nature, Volume 2, Institute in Basic Life Principles, Inc., Box 1, Oak Brook, IL 60522-3001, Rand McNally and Co., 1981.

Character Sketches From the Pages of Scripture Illustrated in the World of Nature, Volume 3, Institute in Basic Life Principles, Inc., Box 1, Oak Brook, IL 60522-3001, Rand McNally and Co., 1985.

Charlie Brown's 'Cyclopedia, New York: Funk and Wagnalls, Inc. 1972.

Children's Encyclopedia of Knowledge, Great Britain: Collins. 1963.

Coe, Geoffrey. *The How and Why Wonder Book of Trees.* USA: Allan Publishers, Inc. 1981.

DeJonge, Joanne E. *Skin and Bones.* Grand Rapids: Baker Book House. 1985.

Drotar, David L. *Fun Science.* New York: Playmore, Inc., Publishers, and Waldman. 1986.

Farb, Peter. *The Insects.* New York: Time Incorporated. 1962.

Fichter, George S. *Insect Pests.* New York: Golden Press. 1966.

Funk and Wagnalls New Encyclopedia of Science, Milwaukee: Raintree. 1986.

Furniss, Tim. *Space Flight: The Records.* Great Britain: Guinness Books. 1985.

Gore, Rick. "Neptune, Voyager's Last Picture Show." *National Geographic* Vol. 178, No. 2, August 1990. Washington D.C.: National Geographic Society.

Gore, Rick. "The Planets, Between Fire and Ice." *National Geographic*, Vol. 167, No. 1, Jan. Washington, D.C.: National Geographic Society. 1985.

Graves,William. "Whales of the World: I. The Imperiled Giants." *National Geographic*, Vol. 150, No. 6, December 1976. Washington, D.C. National Geographic Society.

Grimmer, Glenna Gardiner. *The ABC's of Texas Wildflowers*. Burnet, TX: Eakin Press. 1982.

Hatchett, Clint. *The Glow in the Dark Night Sky Book*. New York: Random House. 1988.

Hegner, Robert W., and Karl A. Stiles. *College Zoology*, 7th Ed. New York: Macmillan. 1959.

Heimler, Charles H. *Focus on Life Science*. Columbus: Charles E. Merril. 1977.

Highland, Dr. Harold J. *Planets and Interplanetary Travel*. New York: Wonder Books. 1962.

How in the World, Pleasantville: Reader's Digest Association, Inc. 1990.

Huxley, Sir Julian, ed. *The Atlas of World Wildlife*, Portland House. 1987.

Illustrated Atlas of the World, New York: Rand McNally. 1984.

Irwin, Howard S. *Roadside Flowers of Texas*. Austin: University of Texas Press. 1982.

Keen, Martin L. *The How and Why Wonder Book of Chemistry*. New York: Grosset & Dunlap. 1961.

Keen, Martin L. *The Human Body*. New York: Grosset and Dunlap. 1982.

Kendeigh, S. Charles. *Animal Ecology*. Englewood Cliffs: Prentice-Hall. 1961.

Lemonick, Michael D. "The Ozone Vanishes." *Time*: February 17, 1992, New York: Time Inc., Magazine Co.

Lepold, Lana B., and Kenneth S. Davis, *Water*. New York: Time Life Books. 1968.

Life Editorial Staff. *The World We Live In*. New York: Simon and Schuster. 1956.

Life—How did it get here? By Evolution or Creation? Brooklyn: Watchtower Bible and Tract Society. 1985.

McConnell, Keith. *The Animalphabet Encyclopedia Coloring Book*. Owings Mills: Stemmer House. 1984.

McGovern, Ann. *The Question and Answer Book about the Human Body*. New York: Random House. 1965.

Miller, G. Tyler Jr. *Living in the Environment*, 3rd ed. Belmont: Wadsworth. 1982.

Miller, Jonathan. *The Human Body*. New York: Viking Press. 1983.

Minelli, Alessandro and Sandro Ruffo, eds. *Great Book of Birds*. New York: Arch Cape Press. 1980.

Moché, Dinah L. *Astronomy Today*. New York: Random House. 1982.

Morris, Henry M. *Science and the Bible*. Chicago: Moody Press. 1986.

Nourse, Alan E. *The Body*. New York: Time Incorporated. 1964.

Octopus Big Book of Nature. London, WI: Octopus Books Limited. 1981.

Ortleb, Edward and Richard Cadice. *Insects*. St. Louis: Milliken. 1968.

Ortleb, Edward, and Richard Cadice. *Amphibians and Reptiles*. St. Louis: Milliken. 1968.

Ortleb, Edward, and Richard Cadice. *Birds*. St. Louis: Milliken. 1968.

Parker, Bertha Morris, ed. *The Golden Book Encyclopedia*. New York: Golden Press. 1960.

Petersen, Dennis. *Unlocking the Mysteries of Creation*. El Dorado, CA: Creation Resource Foundation. 1987.

Peterson, Richard Tory. *The Birds*. New York: Time Incorporated. 1963.

Pfeiffer, John. *The Cell*. New York: Time Incorporated. 1964.

Pough, Frederick H. *A Field Guide to Rocks and Minerals*, 3rd ed. Boston: Houghton Mifflin. 1960.

Richmond, Julius B., et. al. *Health and Growth*. Glenview: Scott, Foresman. 1971.

Robbins, Chandler S., Bertel Bruun, and Herbert S. Zim. *Birds of North America*. New York: Golden Press. 1966.

Rudin, Helen. *The Amazing Question and Answer Book.* New York: Waldman. 1984.

Saunders, John R. *The Question and Answer Book of Nature.* New York: Random House. 1962.

Scheffer, Victor B. "Whales of the World: II. Exploring the Lives of Whales." *National Geographic*, Vol. 150, No. 6, December 1976. Washington, D.C. National Geographic Society.

Silver, Donald M. *Life on Earth, Biology Today.* New York: Random House. 1983.

Smith, Herbert A., et. al. *Modern Science, Level Four.* River Forest: Laidlaw Brothers. 1974.

Starr, Cecie, and Ralph Taggart. *Biology: The Unity and Diversity of Life*, 3rd ed. Belmont: Wadsworth. 1984.

Steele, DeWitt. *Science: Matter and Motion.* Pensacola: A Beka Book Publications. 1981.

Stonehouse, Dr. Bernard. *The Way Your Body Works.* New York: Bonanza Books. 1985.

Swartz, Dr. Steven L., and Mary Lou Jones. "Gray Whales Make a Comeback." *National Geographic*, Vol. 171, No. 6, June 1987. Washington D.C.: National Geographic Society.

The Big Bear Cub Scout Book. Irving, TX: BOY SCOUTS OF AMERICA, 1990.

The Golden Home and High School Encyclopedia, New York: Golden Press. 1961.

The Holy Bible

The Living World, Jane Olliver, Ed., New York: Warwick Press. 1976.

The Monster Book of Questions and Answers, Czechoslovakia: Hamlyn Publishing. 1989.

The New American Desk Encyclopedia, A Signet Book. New York: Penguin Books. 1989.

The World Book Encyclopedia, Chicago: Field Enterprises Educational Corp. 1962.

Thompson, Philip D., and Robert O'Brien, et al. *Weather.* New York: Time Incorporated. 1965.

Tinbergen, Niko. *Animal Behavior.* New York: Time-Life Books. 1965.

Tison, Annette, and Talus Taylor. *The Big Book of Amazing Animal Behavior.* New York: Gosset and Dunlap. 1987.

Vannini, Vanio, and Guiliano Pogliani, eds. *The Color Atlas of Human Anatomy.* New York: Beekman House. 1980.

Vollrath, Fritz. "Spider Webs and Silks." *Scientific American*, Volume 266, No. 3, March 1992. New York: Scientific American.

Webster's Encyclopedia of Dictionaries. USA: Ottenheimer. 1978.

Went, Frits W. *The Plants.* New York: Time Incorporated. 1963.

Whitfield, Dr. Philip, ed. *The Animal Family*, New York: W.W. Norton. 1979.

Wicks, Keith. *Stars and Planets.* New York; Warwick Press. 1977.

Young People's Science Encyclopedia. Chicago: Childrens Press. 1962.

Zim, Hebert S. and Robert H. Baker. *Stars.* New York: Golden Press. 1956.

Zim, Herbert S. , ed. *The Golden Book Encyclopedia of Natural Science*, New York: Golden Press. 1962.

Zim, Herbert S., and Hurst H. Shoemaker, *Fishes.* New York: Golden Press. 1955.

WORD SEARCH ANSWERS

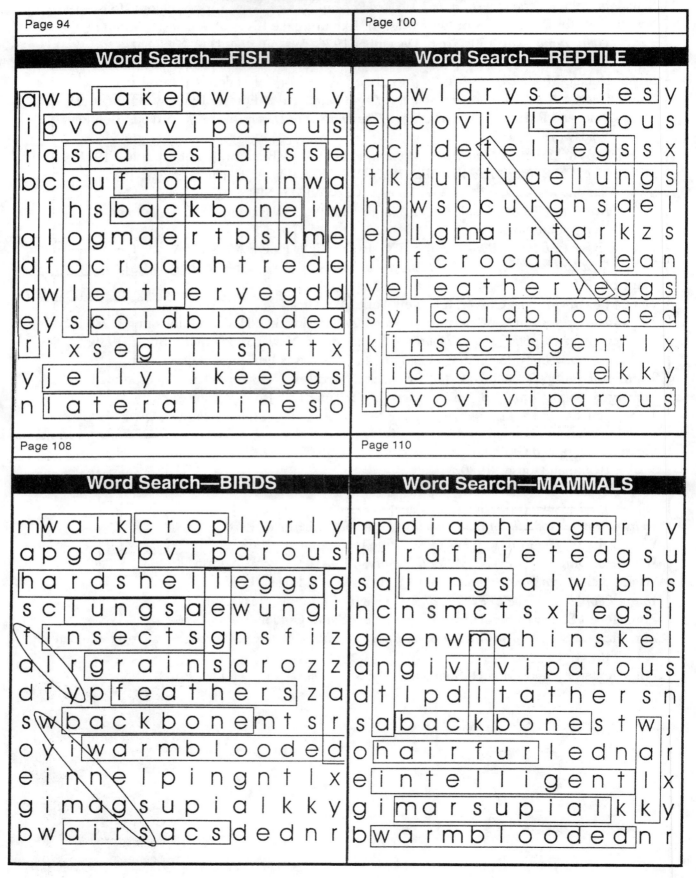

Page 94

Word Search—FISH

```
a w b l a k e a w l y f l y
i p v o v i v i p a r o u s
r a s c a l e s l d f s s e
b c c u f l o a t h i n w a
l i h s b a c k b o n e i w
a l o g m a e r t b s k m e
d f o c r o a a h t r e d e
d w l e a t n e r y e g d d
e y s c o l d b l o o d e d
r i x s e g i l l s n t t x
y j e l l y l i k e e g g s
n l a t e r a l l i n e s o
```

Page 100

Word Search—REPTILE

```
l b w l d r y s c a l e s y
e a c o v i v l a n d o u s
a c r d e t e l l e g s s x
t k a u n t u a e l u n g s
h b w s o c u r g n s a e l
e o l g m a i r f a r k z s
r n f c r o c a h l r e a n
y e l e a t h e r y e g g s
s y l c o l d b l o o d e d
k i n s e c t s g e n t l x
i i c r o c o d i l e k k y
n o v o v i v i p a r o u s
```

Page 108

Word Search—BIRDS

```
m w a l k c r o p l y r l y
a p g o v o v i p a r o u s
h a r d s h e l l e g g s g
s c l u n g s a e w u n g i
f i n s e c t s g n s f i z
a l r g r a i n s a r o z z
d f y p f e a t h e r s z a
s w b a c k b o n e m t s r
o y i w a r m b l o o d e d
e i n n e l p i n g n t l x
g i m a g s u p i a l k k y
b w a i r s a c s d e d n r
```

Page 110

Word Search—MAMMALS

```
m p d i a p h r a g m r l y
h l r d f h i e t e d g s u
s a l u n g s a l w i b h s
h c n s m c t s x l e g s l
g e e n w m a h i n s k e l
a n g i v i v i p a r o u s
d t l p d l t a t h e r s n
s a b a c k b o n e s t w j
o h a i r f u r l e d n a r
e i n t e l l i g e n t l x
g i m a r s u p i a l k k y
b w a r m b l o o d e d n r
```

Crossword Answers

Page 245

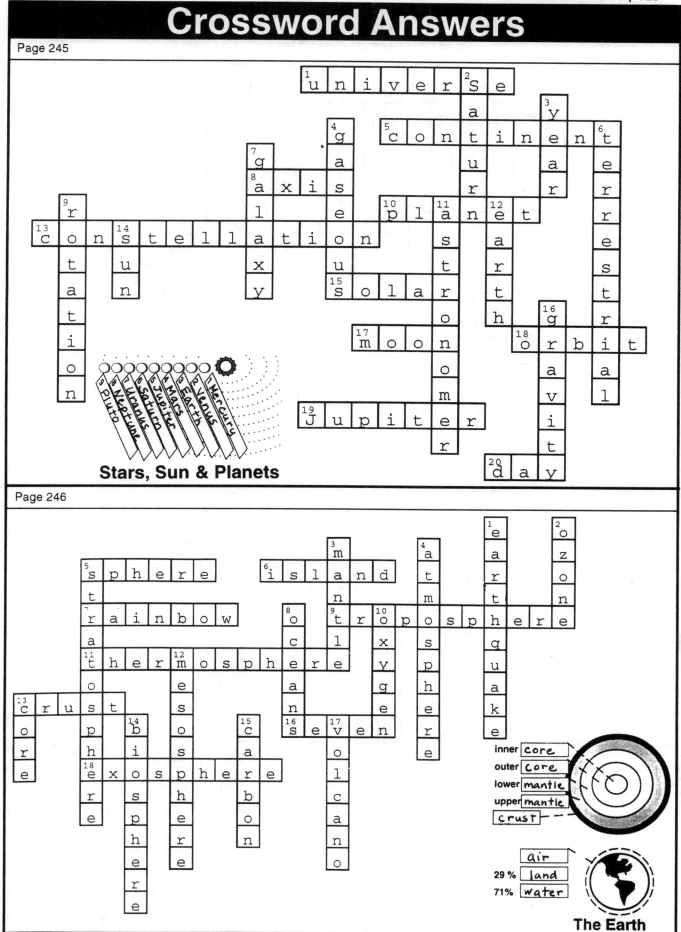

Stars, Sun & Planets

Page 246

inner core
outer core
lower mantle
upper mantle
crust

air
29% land
71% water

The Earth

Crossword Answers

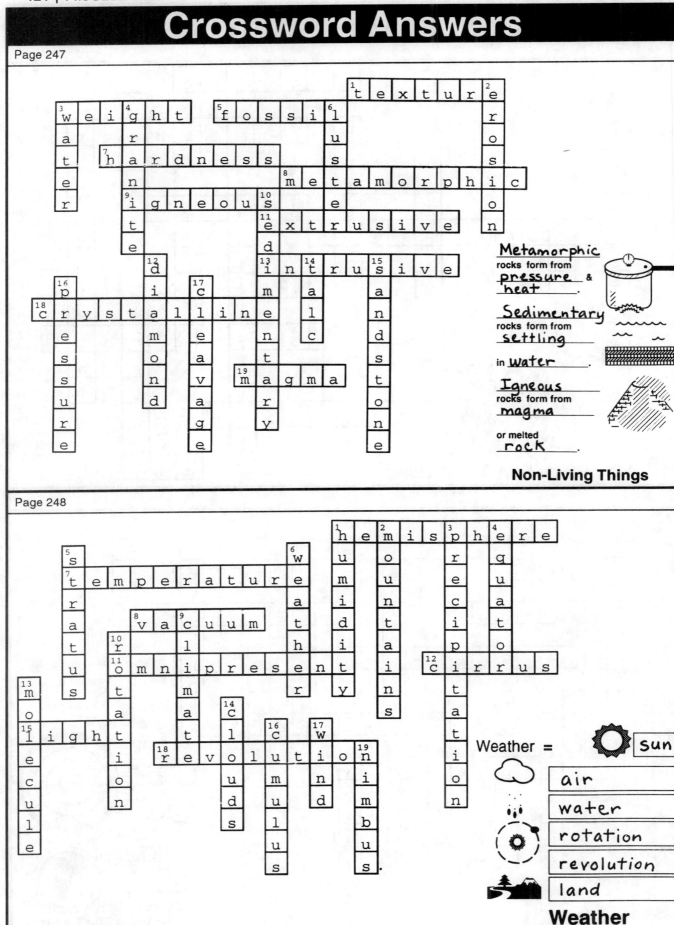

Non-Living Things

Metamorphic rocks form from **pressure** & **heat**.

Sedimentary rocks form from **settling** in **water**.

Igneous rocks form from **magma** or melted **rock**.

Weather = **sun**, **air**, **water**, **rotation**, **revolution**, **land**

Weather

Crossword Answers

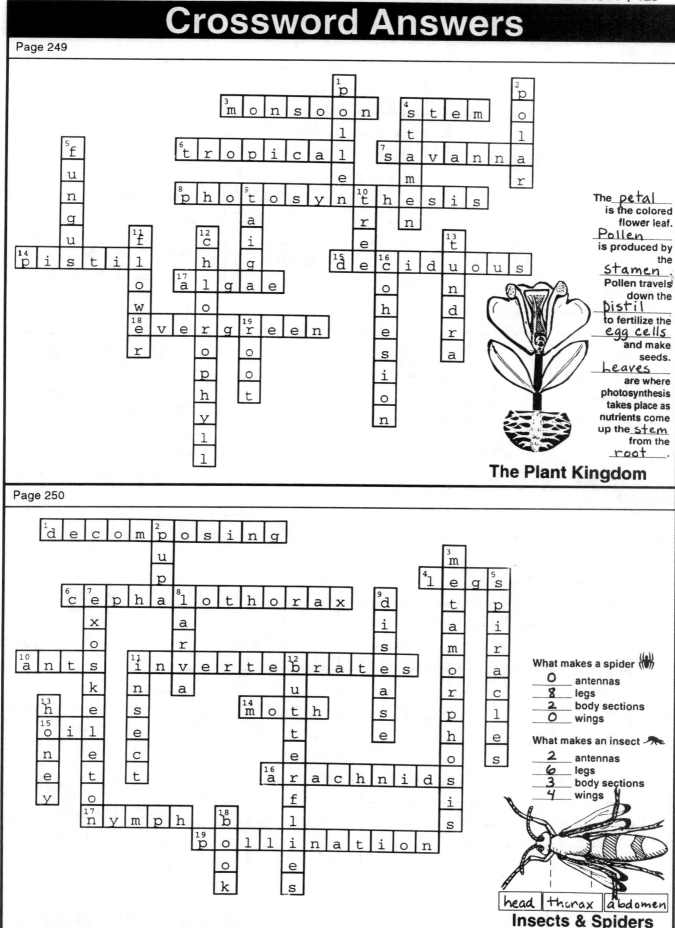

Page 249

3 m o n s o o n
4 s t e m
1 p o l l e n
2 p o l a r

6 t r o p i c a l
7 s a v a n n a

8 p h o t o s y n t h e s i s

14 p i s t i l

17 a l g a e

18 e v e r g r e e n

15 d e c i d u o u s

The _petal_ is the colored flower leaf.

Pollen is produced by the _stamen_.

Pollen travels down the _pistil_ to fertilize the _egg cells_ and make seeds.

Leaves are where photosynthesis takes place as nutrients come up the _stem_ from the _root_.

The Plant Kingdom

Page 250

1 d e c o m p o s i n g

6 c e p h a l o t h o r a x

10 a n t s

11 i n v e r t e b r a t e s

14 m o t h

16 a r a c h n i d

17 n y m p h

19 p o l l i n a t i o n

What makes a spider
- 0 antennas
- 8 legs
- 2 body sections
- 0 wings

What makes an insect
- 2 antennas
- 6 legs
- 3 body sections
- 4 wings

head | thorax | abdomen

Insects & Spiders

Crossword Answers

Page 251

Fish are cold blooded, have scales & fins, breathe through gills and lay jelly-like eggs. Reptiles are cold blooded, have dry, scaly skin, breathe through lungs and lay leathery eggs. Birds are warm blooded, have feathers & wings, breathe through lungs and lay hard shell eggs. Mammals are warm blooded, have hair or fur, breathe through lungs and have live births and milk for their young. Amphibians are cold blooded, eggs hatch in water then move to land, breathe first through gills and later through lungs.

Fish, Reptiles, Birds, Mammals & Amphibians

Page 252

Match the definition to the word:

a. ecosystem ___6___
b. gene ___4___
c. omnivore ___7___
d. reproduce ___9___
e. recessive ___5___
f. dominate ___8___
g. ligaments ___10___
h. carnivore ___1___
i. antlers ___2___
j. nutrient ___3___
k. sterile ___12___
l. oviparous ___11___
m. paleontologist ___18___
n. muscles ___19___
o. viviparous ___9___
p. skeleton ___14___
q. herbivore ___17___
r. horns ___15___
s. heredity ___16___
t. fertile ___20___

Animal Anatomy & Physiology (1)

Crossword Answers

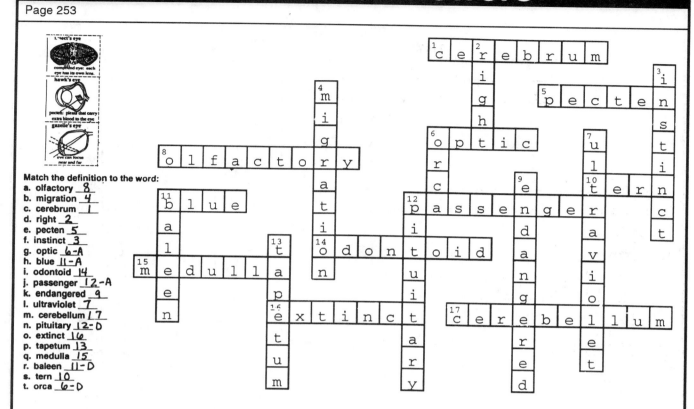

Match the definition to the word:

a. olfactory _8_
b. migration _4_
c. cerebrum _1_
d. right _2_
e. pecten _5_
f. instinct _3_
g. optic _6-A_
h. blue _11-A_
i. odontoid _14_
j. passenger _12-A_
k. endangered _9_
l. ultraviolet _7_
m. cerebellum _17_
n. pituitary _12-D_
o. extinct _16_
p. tapetum _13_
q. medulla _15_
r. baleen _11-D_
s. tern _10_
t. orca _6-D_

Animal Anatomy & Physiology (2)

Draw a line from the word to its location in the cell.

a. cell membrane
b. mitochondria
c. lysosomes
d. DNA
e. nucleus
f. centrioles
g. Golgi bodies
h. chromosomes

Man: Reproductive System & The Cell

Crossword Answers

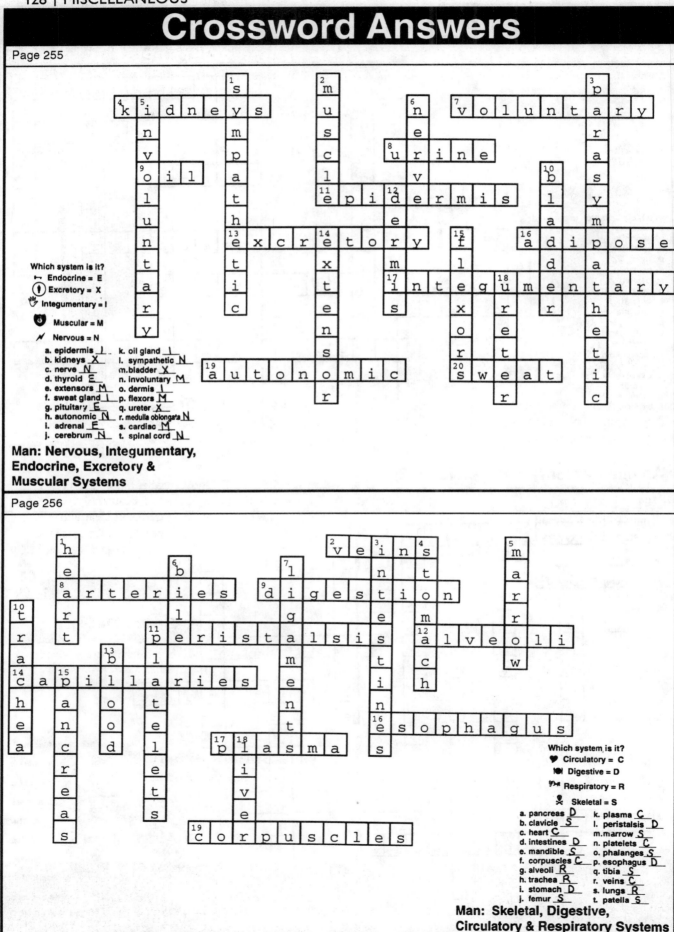

Which system is it?
- ↤ Endocrine = E
- Excretory = X
- Integumentary = I
- Muscular = M
- Nervous = N

a. epidermis **I**
b. kidneys **X**
c. nerve **N**
d. thyroid **E**
e. extensors **M**
f. sweat gland **I**
g. pituitary **E**
h. autonomic **N**
i. adrenal **E**
j. cerebrum **N**

k. oil gland **I**
l. sympathetic **N**
m. bladder **X**
n. involuntary **M**
o. dermis **I**
p. flexors **M**
q. ureter **X**
r. medulla oblongata **N**
s. cardiac **M**
t. spinal cord **N**

Man: Nervous, Integumentary, Endocrine, Excretory & Muscular Systems

Which system is it?
- ♥ Circulatory = C
- Digestive = D
- Respiratory = R
- Skeletal = S

a. pancreas **D**
b. clavicle **S**
c. heart **C**
d. intestines **D**
e. mandible **S**
f. corpuscles **C**
g. alveoli **R**
h. trachea **R**
i. stomach **D**
j. femur **S**

k. plasma **C**
l. peristalsis **D**
m. marrow **S**
n. platelets **C**
o. phalanges **S**
p. esophagus **D**
q. tibia **S**
r. veins **C**
s. lungs **R**
t. patella **S**

Man: Skeletal, Digestive, Circulatory & Respiratory Systems

Science

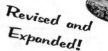
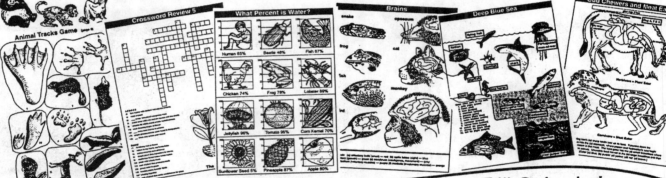
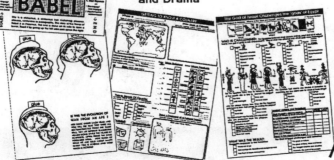

Phonics

Alphabet Island Phonics

#1 - Kindergarten

Young students will love this program! Each 15 minute lesson has a song, poem, game, blackboard and workbook activity, all geared toward optimum learning. The students master the phonetic sounds, alphabetic sequence, correct letter formation and the reading and spelling of more than 230 three-letter short-vowel words. Alphabet Island Phonics 1 comes with step-by-step teacher's manual, student workbook, flash cards, games, laminated four-color alphabet flash cards and a CD.

Price $69.95
Additional Workbook $9.95

#2 - 1st to 9th

Alphabet Island Phonics is the most thorough, effective and creative phonics and spelling program available, giving your children what they need to be competent readers and exceptional spellers. It comes complete with step-by-step teacher's manuals, student workbooks, flash cards, games and a CD. Most importantly, **Alphabet Island Phonics** instills an absolute love and enjoyment of reading and spelling.

Price $84.95
Additional Workbooks $14.95

Comprehensive Handbook of Phonics

Kindergarten - 9th Grade

- 86 Word Charts
- Teacher's Manual
- Penmanship
- Creative Writing Course
- 50 Book Report Ideas

- 25 Spelling/Reading games
- 64 Phonogram flash cards
- Creative teaching helps
- 600 most often used sight words

$19.95

Order Today!

Name:

Street:

City: **State:**

Zip: **Telephone:**

Quantity	Item	Price	Total
	Considering God's Creation (**FREE** audio CD)	$29.95	
	Alphabet Island Phonics Complete (**BEST BUY!**) Includes Alphabet Island Phonics 1 &2 (**FREE** Kinder-Math and EW Handbook of Phonics)	$119.95	
	Alphabet Island Phonics 1 (**FREE** Kinder-Math)	$69.95	
	Alphabet Island Phonics 2 (**FREE** EW Handbook of Phonics)	$84.95	
	Kinder-Math	$14.95	
	It's a Capital Game	$4.95	
	Vol. 1: Remembering God's Awesome Acts	$35.00	
	Vol. 2: Remembering God's Chosen Children	$35.00	
Additional Workbooks, CD's, and Tapes			
	Alphabet Island Phonics Level 1 wkbk	$9.95	
	Alphabet Island Phonics Level 2 wkbks	$14.95	
	Kinder-Math wkbk	$4.95	
	Considering God's Creation wkbk	$13.95	
	Vol. 1: Remembering God's Awesome Acts wkbk	$20.00	
	Vol. 2: Remembering God's Chosen Children wkbk	$20.00	
	Considering God's Creation Audio CD	$3.00	
	Considering God's Creation Cassette	$3.00	
	Alphabet Island Phonics Audio CD	$3.00	
	Alphabet Island Phonics Cassette	$3.00	
	Alphabet Island Alphabet Flash Cards	$3.00	
Other Items			
	Eagle's Wings Comprehensive Handbook of Phonics	$19.95	
	Subtotal		
	Shipping USA: up to $35—Add $3.50 $36 to $110—Add $5.50 $111 and up—Add 5% Double above rates for UPS. (Contact us for International Rates.)		
	Tax (Oklahoma only: 5.05%; include tax on shipping)		
	Total		

Order by credit card at (580) 252-1555 or on-line NOW at **www.eagleswingsed.com**
Most orders are shipped by US Postal Service within 24 hours. Or send your check or money order (US funds only) to: **Eagle's Wings Educational Materials**
PO Box 502, Duncan, OK 73534

SATISFACTION GUARANTEED! Money-back guarantee when returned in good condition within 30 days (less postage and 10% restocking fee).

Please send _____ brochures for my friends.
I heard about you from:

❑ Homeschool card deck   ❑ Literature bag from convention   ❑ Friend
❑ Internet _____   ❑ Other _____

Give your child a solid start in math with ...

Kinder-Math

Worksheets, flashcards, and word problems teach:
➜ Formation of numbers with poems
➜ Counting to 100 by 1's, 2's, 5's and 10's.
➜ > Greater than, < Less than, = Equal to
➜ Simple addition facts
➜ Simple geometry   ➜ Money
➜ Telling time   ➜ Sequence

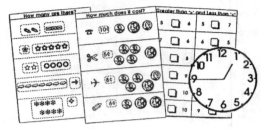

"Kinder-Math is well-designed sequentially. The best part of this program is the excellent teaching sequence, activities and instructions in the teacher's manual." —**Mary Pride**

To State It Simply It's a Capital Game

Your child will easily learn all 50 states and capitals with this fun game using captivating cartoons and clever puns. The game comes as a booklet with cut-apart flashcards.
(Actual card size 3 3/4" x 5")

Answer: Austin, Texas

Answer: Boise, Idaho

Answer: Augusta, Maine

In 1987, two homeschooling families launched Eagle's Wings Educational Materials from their homes. We wanted to provide the homeschooling community with materials designed to help YOU stimulate your children's thinking, creativity, and learning. By God's grace and your support, we're still at it. THANK YOU!